The H. P. LOVECRAFT
Coloring, dot-to-dot, & activity book

Illustrations by
Nigel Dobbyn

ARCTURUS

ARCTURUS

This edition published in 2017 by Arcturus Publishing Limited
26/27 Bickels Yard, 151–153 Bermondsey Street,
London SE1 3HA

Copyright © Arcturus Holdings Limited

ISBN: 978-1-78428-605-7
CH005408NT
Supplier 29, Date 0417, Print Run 5865

Printed in China

INTRODUCTION

For years, the dark and ingenious world of H. P. Lovecraft's creations has both fascinated and terrified horror fiction fans all over the world—and now they will delight lovers of puzzles and activities too. There is something timeless and universal in the strange and unsettling imagery of Lovecraft's stories that gels so well with the quiet solitude needed to complete these fantastic activities.

Each of these puzzles, dot-to-dot drawings, and fabulous artworks for coloring in has been custom made to reflect the grizzly imaginings of H. P. Lovecraft. All you need is a pen, some paints or colored pencils, and a moment to yourself in order to delve into this gruesome world of otherworldly horrors.

With such a variety of ghoulish activities to choose from, there are hours of fun to be had for fans of all ages. In case any of them are unfamiliar to you, here's a brief guide to completing them.

Hanjie

Reveal a hidden picture by solving the Hanjie puzzles in this book, which appear on pages 7, 18, 30, 42, 54, 66, 78, 90, 102, and 114. Numbers at the start of each row or column reveal, in order from left to right or top to bottom, the length of each consecutive run of shaded squares. There must be a gap of at least one empty square between adjacent runs of shaded squares in the same row or column. For example, a clue with a single number tells you how many consecutive shaded squares there are in the row or column, and all other squares in that row/column must be unshaded.

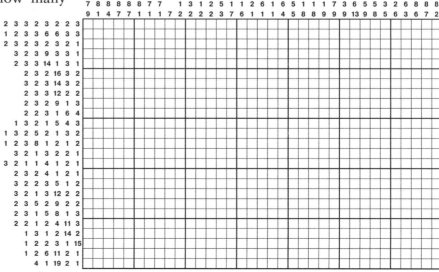

If a clue was "5,4" then there would be 5 consecutive shaded squares, a gap of 1 or more squares, and then 4 consecutive shaded squares in that row or column—and all other squares would remain unshaded. Here are some helpful tips:

- As well as shading squares, you should also mark squares you know must be unshaded too. Writing a small 'x' in them works well.

- Work back and forth between rows and columns, cross-referencing information.

- There's never any need to guess—logic alone is all you need!

Mazes

Find your way through each maze from the entrance marked with an arrow at the top to the exit at the bottom. In the bridge mazes the path crosses under or over itself at the marked bridges. You'll find three types of mazes in this book, standard mazes on pages 9, 21, 33, and 45; circular mazes on pages 57, 69, and 81, and finally bridge mazes on pages 93, 105, and 117.

Samurai Sudoku

Place the numbers 1 to 9 into each row, column and 3x3 box of each of the 13 overlapping grids. Work back and forth between overlapping grids to find the unique overall solution. These puzzles are to be found on pages 14, 26, 38, 50, 62, 74, 86, 98, and 110.

Wordsearch

Find all of the listed entries in the grid. They may be written in any direction, including diagonally, and may read either forward or backward. These puzzles appear on pages 13, 25, 37, 49, 61, 73, 85, 97, and 109.

```
E U T N A S I S L T M A D H U O U E L E
M A E E H A U R S E H S D T I M U R U D
M T O S D N Y L M P Y E T O C T O P U S
S H W N O D W C L A P N U A T E D A H N
E U E A H G W T W L R E N O T D I W A O
N R I H Y A N R O A T E L P N R E M S E
O S R O H E O L N H P O I A E E U H C C
D T D J A N S G E I A R L T N H L E U N
L O T H E A E A N S C S S U A L I L L D
O N A R A L L C A S I Y E U L O T H P R
T Y L S L E E I U D H U S S O I S T T A
A S E C R Y L N E S T X W S S X I W U G
E S S T L A A T S D M D N T O A A O R O
R T S G R M R A E O H E S N A L R N E N
G U T T L A M C A S S U R N U T I G I I
O E S C H E T H E E M M A S A T W P E E
S U I C A D E I A S A C W I L C O X O L
A G N A N A E D I L C U E N O N L E N L
R U L U R I T U A L E E U H W I M D C H
T H T A H C C S C A S H A I H E Y L R L
```

Dot-to-dots

Each image is made up of 300–400 numbered dots. Simply start by locating the first dot and let your line progress from one number to the next, in ascending order. Some puzzles contain additional lines so if there are lower-case letters then you should also join these in order from 'a' to 'z', and if there are upper case letters, join these in order from 'A' to 'Z' too. All you need is a sharp pencil or pen and a straight edge to draw against for the long lines, and, hey presto, you have created an incredible image.

There is a full set of solutions to all of the puzzles at the back of the book in case you need a helping hand.

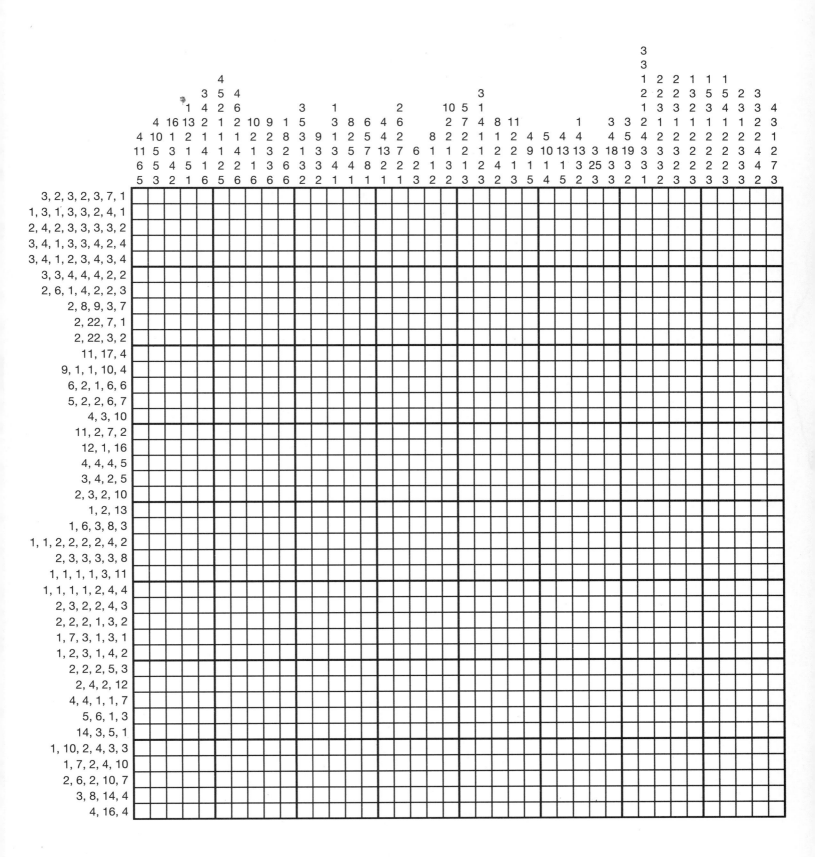

H.P. Lovecraft Short Stories

```
T T T H E T E M P L E H O E O A H O B A
O T H T M T H E U N N A M A B L E E S T
E U H H O S N E O L E U I Y D A E L I R
E I E E S R D I S T T N R T G V S T O A
A D R T S E V P W H T P D I L I T L E H
U T I O S I K F E H U N I C N T H B A T
U M A M L D L M E H O N N S D S E S R L
N H L B H U O V T Y Y E N S T E C D H U
F T O I T O A G E A C H V E M F A T A F
M X O L N U H B R R T B O L D E L H T O
E E C B L Y M L M E K A P E S H L E R S
T L O T H O A L E S H E I M O T O O T T
N G A E R T O R N H C T Y A N E F U H A
H H X F H B T A G S E A O N P E C T S C
E O D O H S H U A L T G R E Y O T S A E
H Y T M E R E O R H I R T H H T H I U H
S E T H L R T L D G E Y H T A T U D A T
P F T L U E R A E F G N I K R U L E H T
H O O H H H E H E E L U A C Y U H R G U
B H A R N T E T V A D H N F O S U A B N
```

COOL AIR
EX OBLIVIONE
FROM BEYOND
HYPNOS
IN THE VAULT
NYARLATHOTEP
SWEET ERMENGARDE
THE CALL OF CTHULHU
THE CATS OF ULTHAR
THE FESTIVAL
THE LURKING FEAR

THE MOON-BOG
THE NAMELESS CITY
THE OTHER GODS
THE OUTSIDER
THE SHUNNED HOUSE
THE SILVER KEY
THE STREET
THE TEMPLE
THE TOMB
THE TREE
THE UNNAMABLE

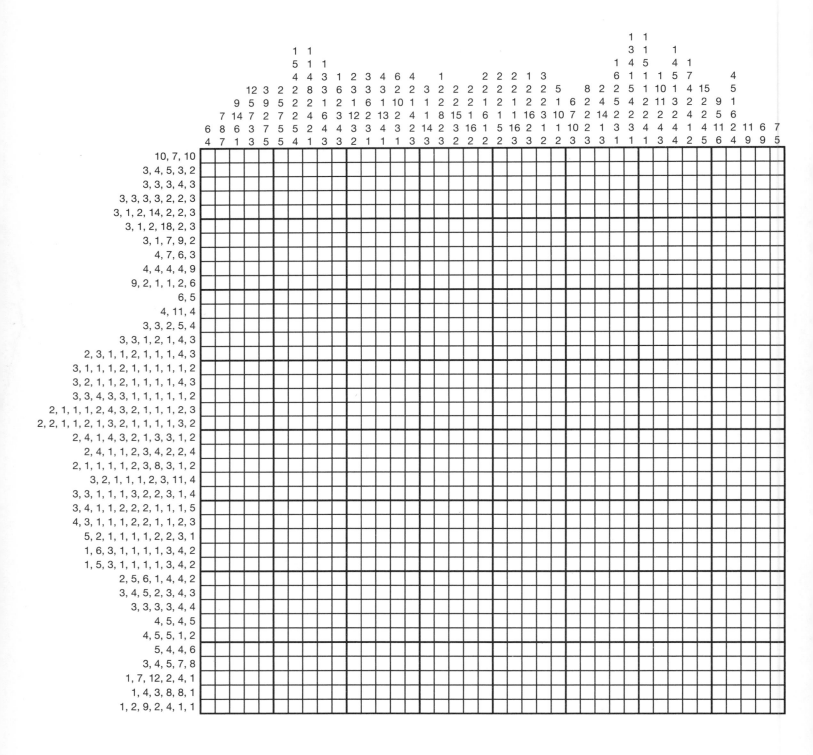

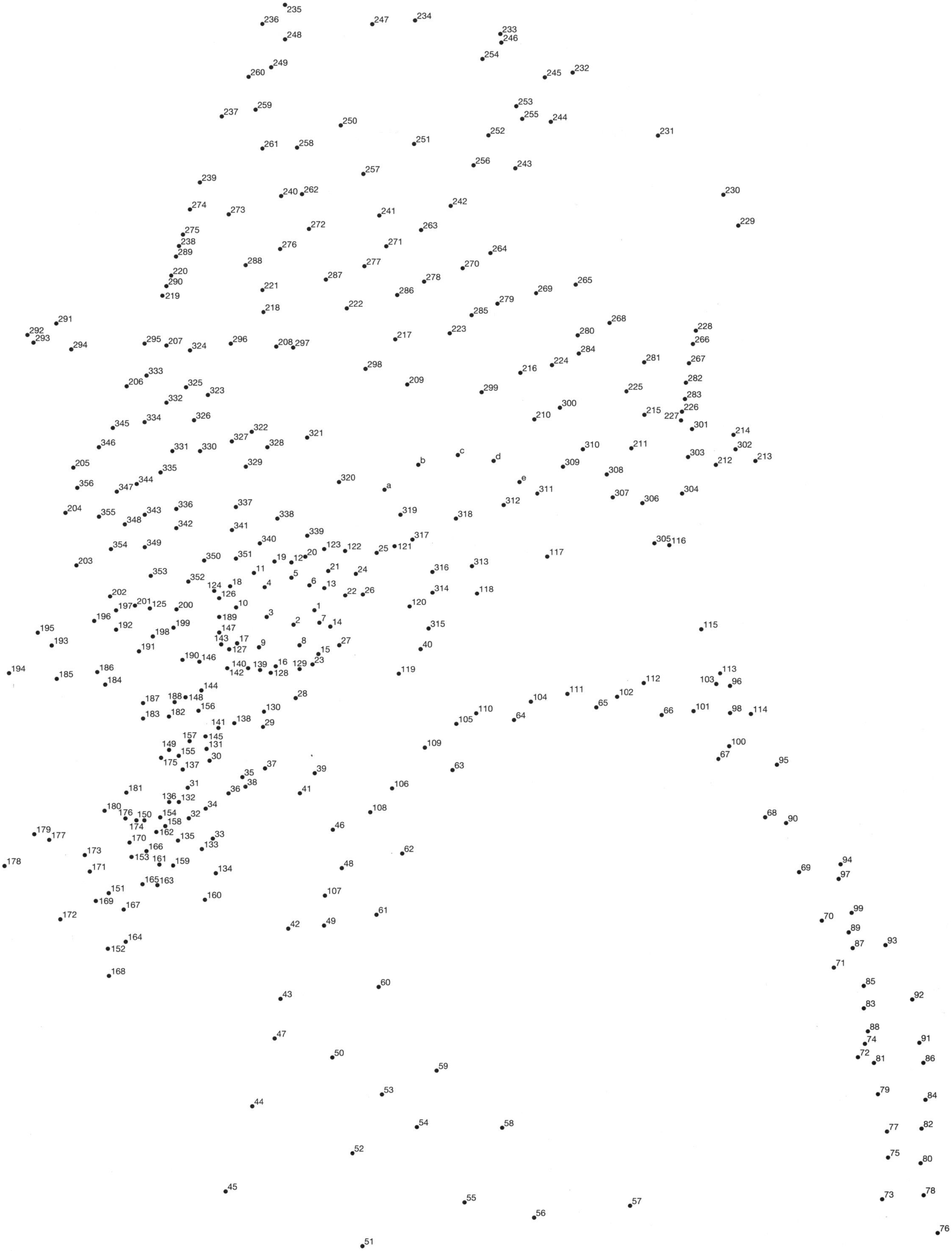

Lovecraft Species

```
N S R R O T O E S H H A A R G A Y V R S
A O A D N E O L T A G U G O N B T G T T
I L A N P R G N A R E T P O E L O C H P
H A N T K O N T D E B A A L G E M B E T
T D D N B A T U T N N O N R H S B U P O
I N E A N N T O D R H A O N H H O A U
D I E G N O P H K E H U E R S O E P E D
D T S H O T T A K G G F A R L G R O T I
A F E B U A R A V O H O I O R G D T I A
Y O D H P K T U G D K E I H B O H H H O
E D T C Y N B E N H A G G G T T T E W B
S N A N A P H A G O R A S N F H I E T D
H U A H E V E E E A C A H I L L N H E D
G O S T A H E R A E H E N T T R O O O F
G H A E I R Y B B R H R H N L U O H G G
L N T K Y T O U E O Y K U U U T V N O O
H O S N R O H D G A R T A H G I H T O E
T O A N P O N S O G S E W Y T C T E H R
E H H N O F H N A T A T A H B H U H D S
O A G N O R R I H D H O T N G N W E O G
```

BUOPOTH
BYAKHEE
CAVE BEAST
COLEOPTERAN
GHAST
GHOUL
GNOPHKEH
GNORRI
GUG
HOUND OF TINDALOS
HUNTING HORROR

HYPERBOREAN
RAANDEESE
SHANTAK
SHOGGOTH
TITAN
TOMB HERD
URHAG
VOONITH
WHITE APE
YADDITHIAN
YUGG

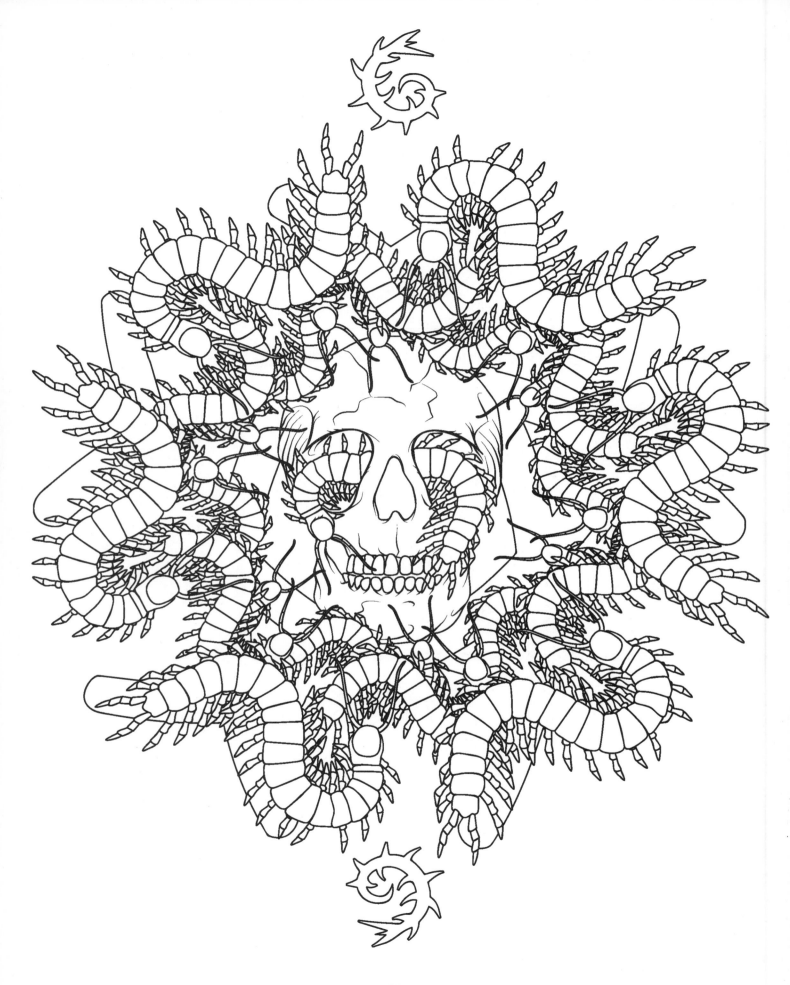

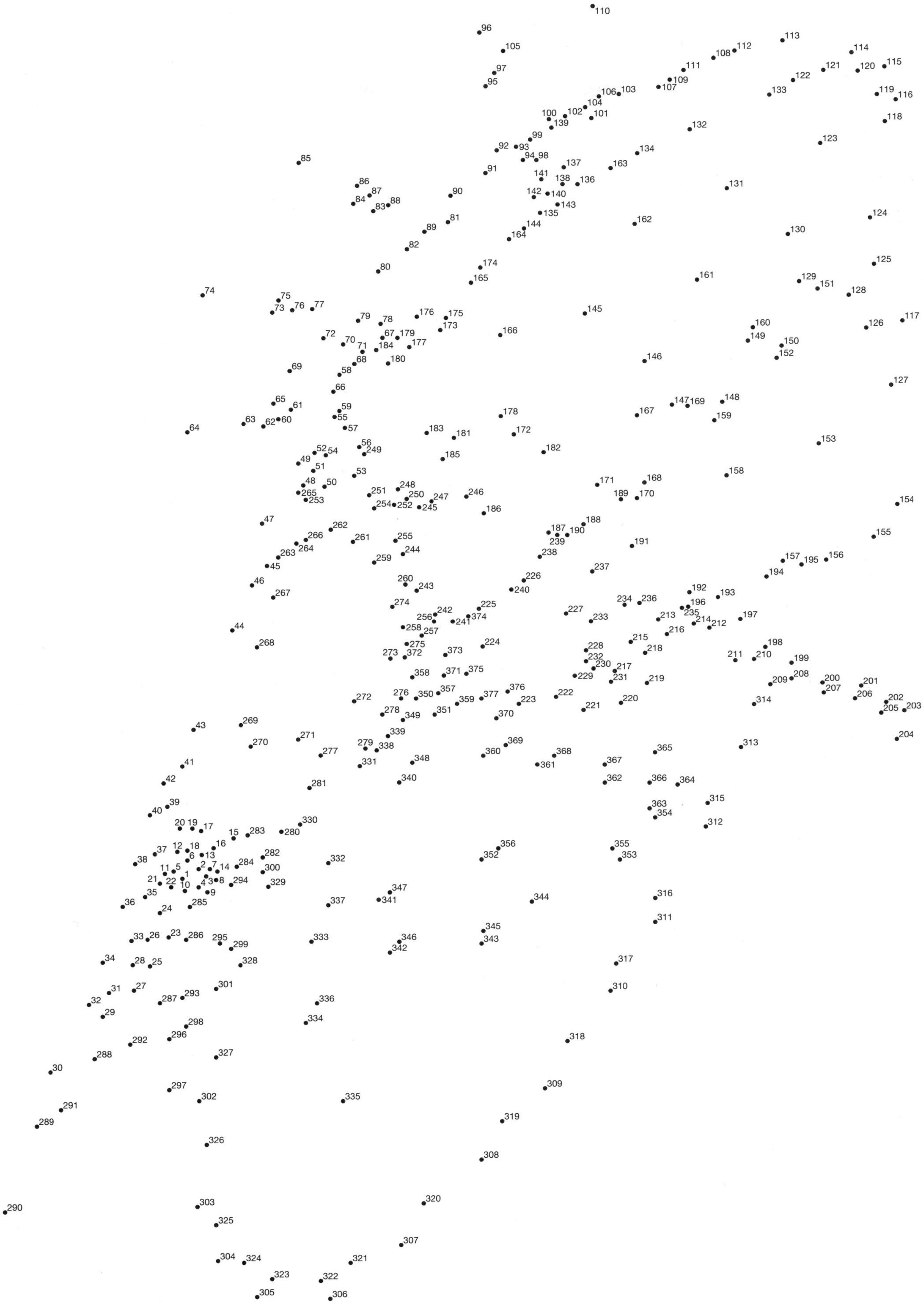

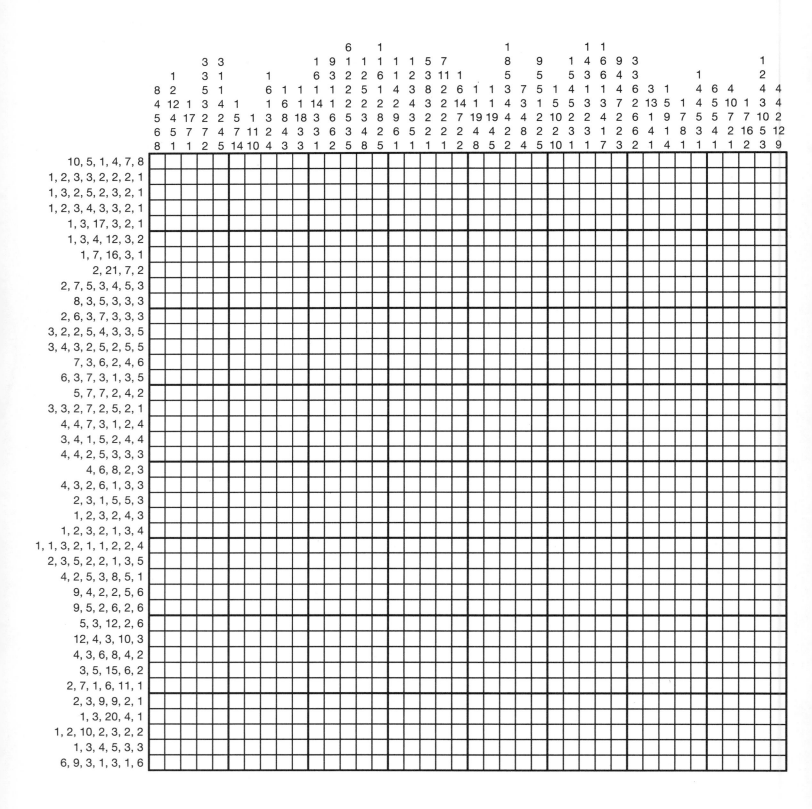

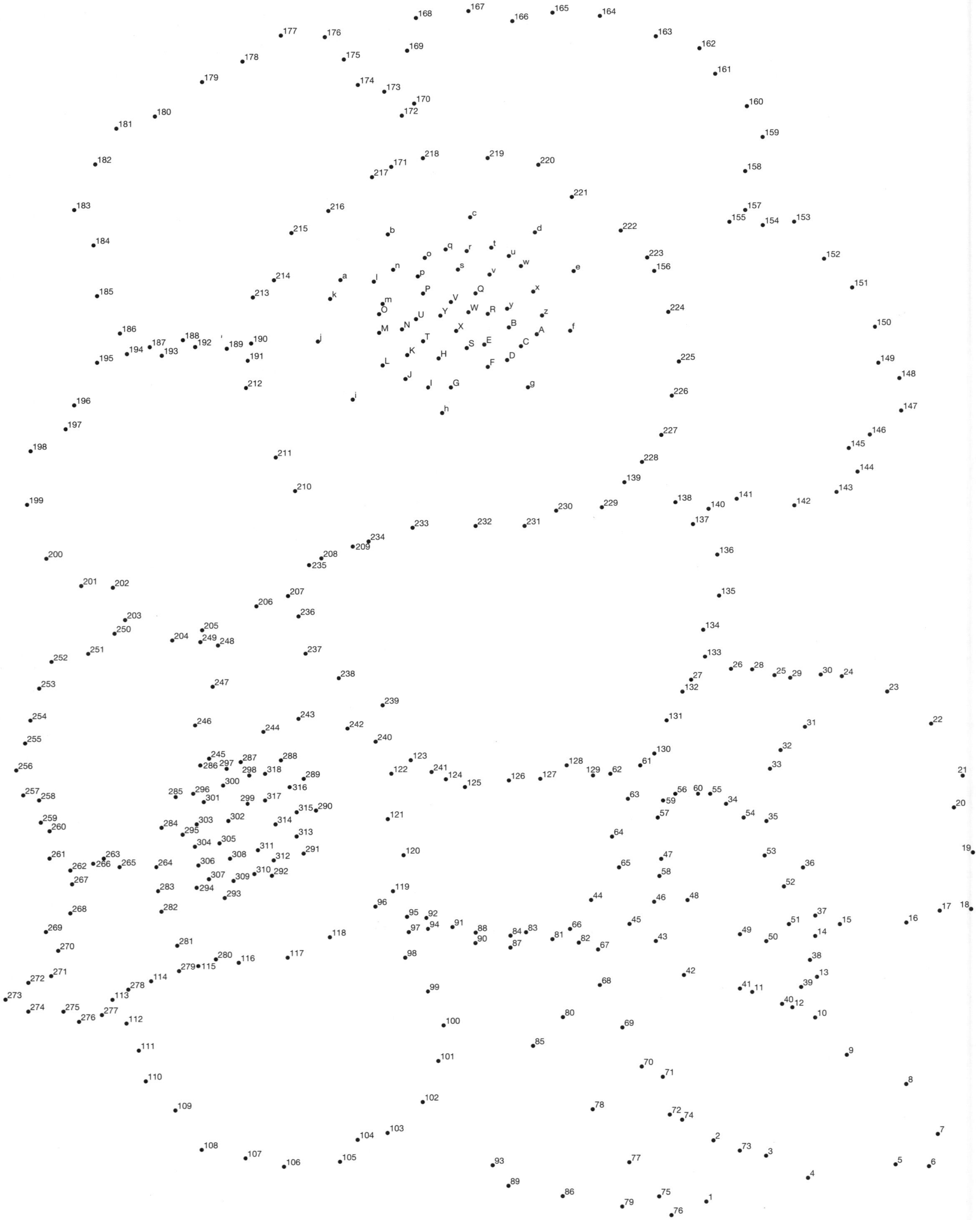

Lovecraftian Writers

```
C D O O E Y A R Y H O T R U T N M S R D
T H U S E Y R O B E R T B L O C H B U W
T R S A R M Z B P L E E D Y E T N P B C
Y T T T E E N E E R G H A I N O S E D E
L E E H F A B R A H A M M E R R I T T O
K H L K E O R M L L W E A T Y N T E N P
W T A M N N R J A H I O S K S H A R A L
O E L Z U U R C A H R A A R A A A O C R K
L L E W E L L Y N M C A B O S B P A G E
R R R A H L M P S E E W M I L E R N H N
A E O T A L H A D W L S T R S M M N T H
B D O R T I N E I R H E F R H H A O E Z
H T M H A S H F A L A I H M E H O N N O
R S L R K P A E T L L W T A O B T P N O
E U C Y L K R L R A D I D E N R O T E E
N G E O E W Y U A R A R W E H N T R K F
W U D U A N E W R I M E L I S E A O L E
R A M S E Y C A M P B E L L S H A D N H
H P N B E R O B E R T E H O W A R D A O
S A H L G H S S A T C M H P B G M H H R
```

ABRAHAM MERRITT	KENNETH GRANT
ADOLPHE DE CASTRO	LLEWELLYN M CABOS
ANNA HELEN CROFTS	PETER CANNON
ANSKY	R H BARLOW
AUGUST DERLETH	RAMSEY CAMPBELL
C L MOORE	ROBERT BLOCH
DUANE W RIMEL	ROBERT E HOWARD
EDWARD PLUNKETT	ROBERT W CHAMBERS
HAZEL HEALD	SONIA H GREENE
HENRY S WHITEHEAD	WILLIAM LUMLEY
JAMES F MORTON	ZEALIA BISHOP

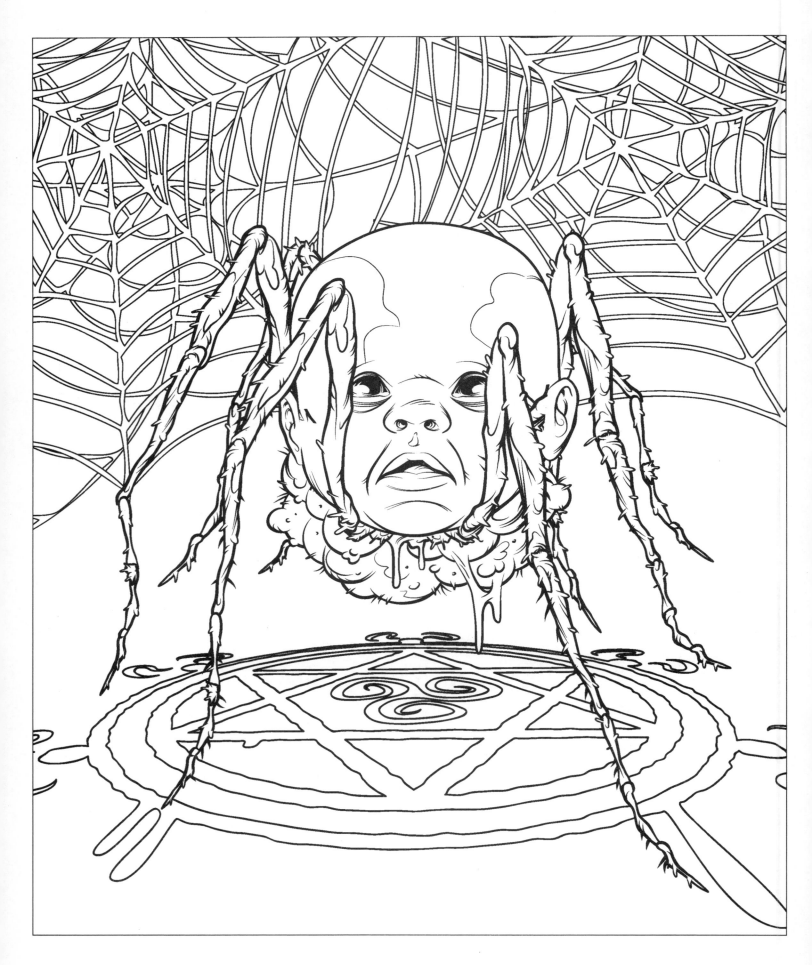

41

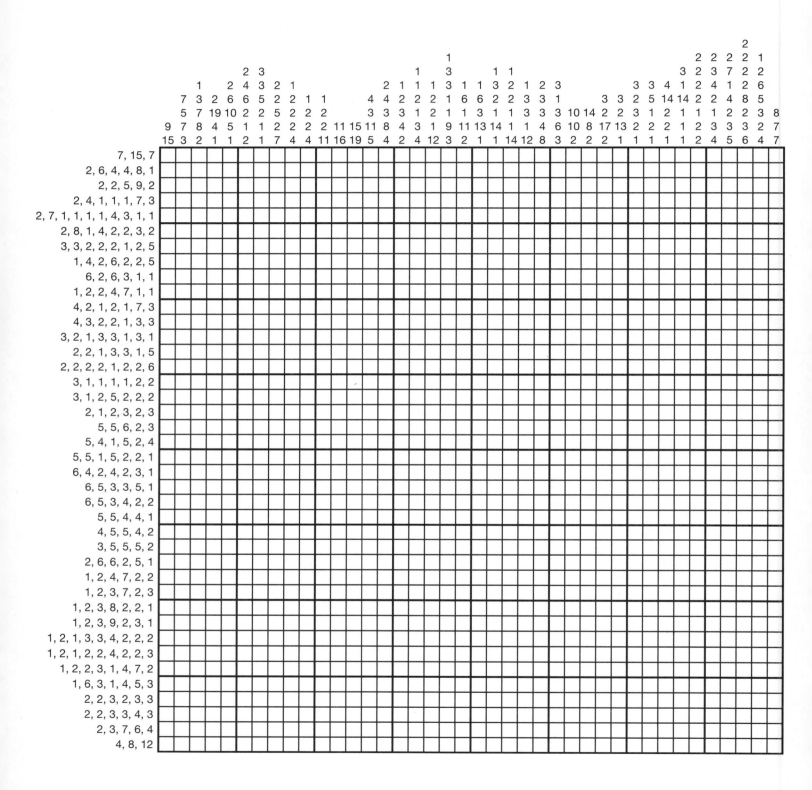

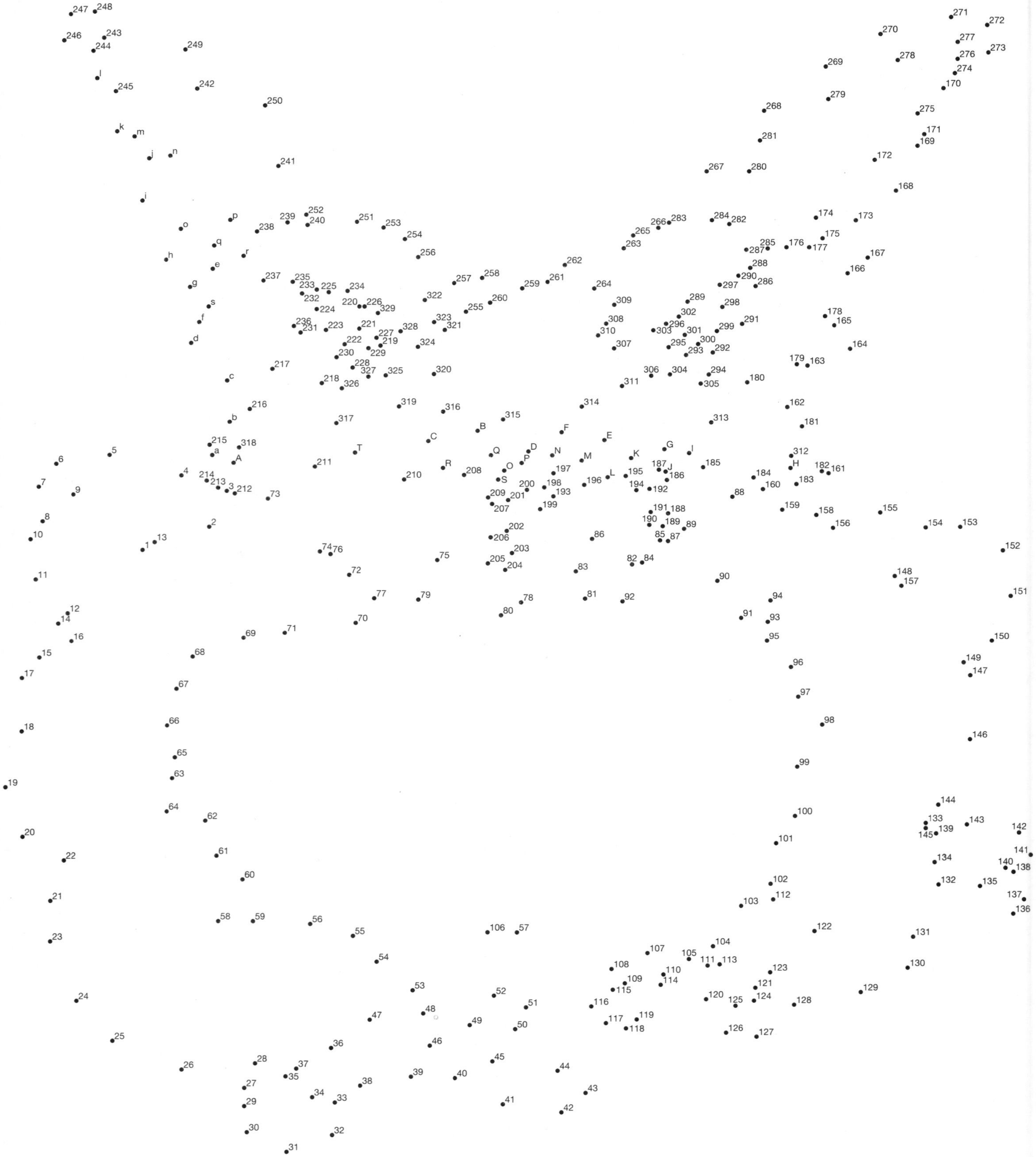

The Fungi From Yuggoth

```
R E T T T L L I H S N A M A Z D T H L T
Y Y Y T I U N I T N O C A H R L E A H N
T H I N L E Y N T Z A T A A Z I I E H N
L T T U G A T U R N H E Y T T T L T S H
I H I T H M N Y H E R T H H T A O H S I
E E U T Y N T A F I R E E U M H A H I N
L H S W L M T A N U D C R P T I N H I F
A O R A T N M H O W A P A A S H E Y T S
C W U E O I Y C E N L O Z T A S F R F N
S L P H L D E L A E E A N S P O E E O O
R E E I O H L L T E L U T E S C N O R I
E R A A T E A R R S A D R N O T E H I T
R R A E R S T U T G M I E G O G T E Y A
S D A E R U T A T S A D N R A E I S E N
A N T A A P R H H O R I E R P S A F K E
A U E S A W G W M A T L I T L H H H T E I
O P R C I I O H G I U M I G A G A A H L
S T E N N I D E O E K H N N N N O T R T A
H R D N T N H N H T H E B E L L S T O G
C S L H E T S S O T K R A T N A T H S S
```

ALIENATION

ANTARKTOS

AZATHOTH

CONTINUITY

HESPERIA

MIRAGE

NIGHT-GAUNTS

PURSUIT

RECAPTURE

RECOGNITION

STAR-WINDS

THE BELLS

THE CANAL

THE COURTYARD

THE DWELLER

THE ELDER PHAROS

THE FAMILIARS

THE GARDENS OF YIN

THE HOWLER

THE KEY

THE LAMP

ZAMAN'S HILL

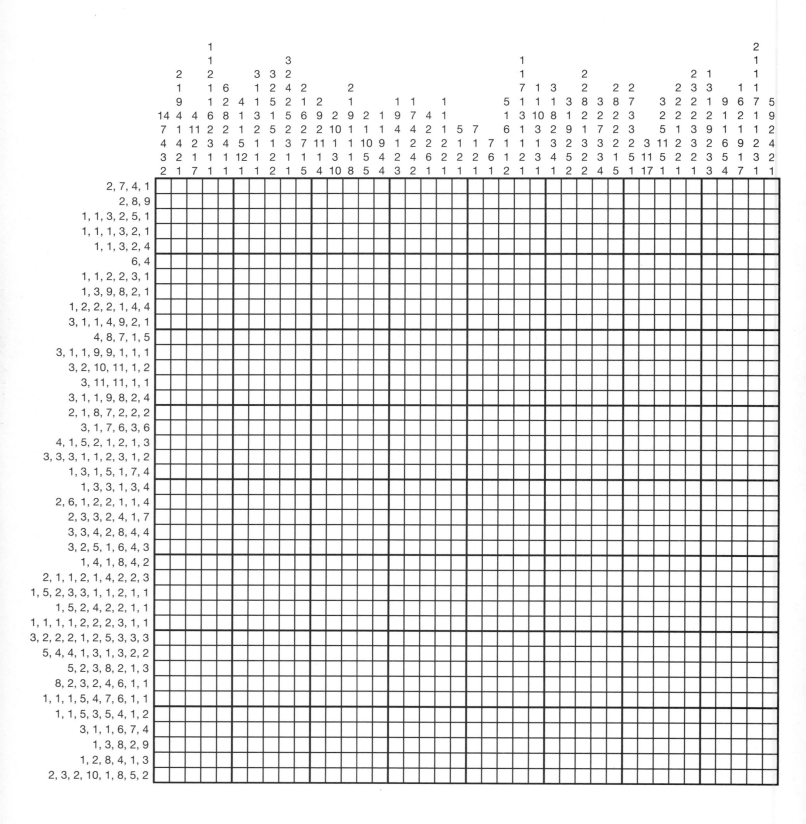

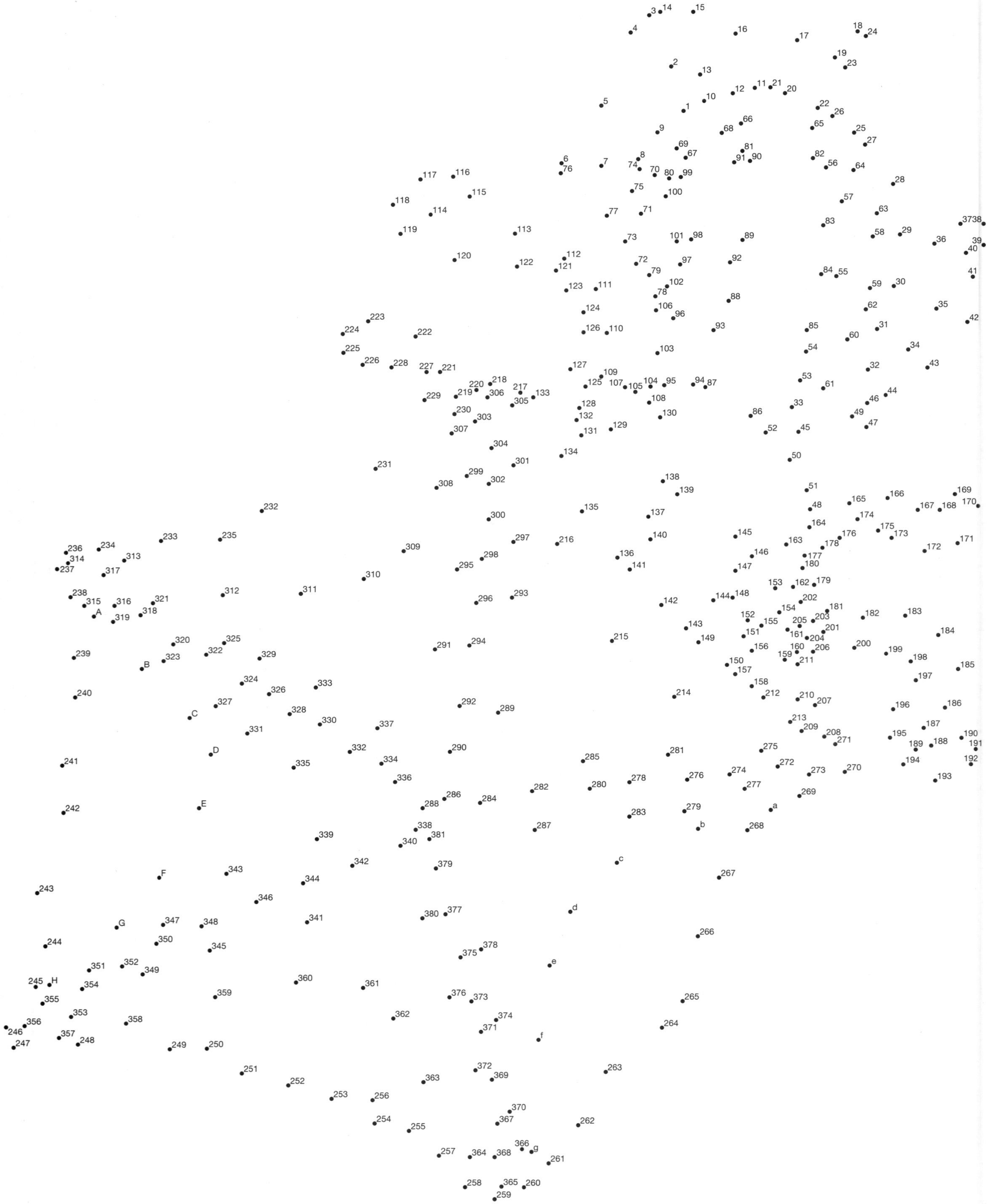

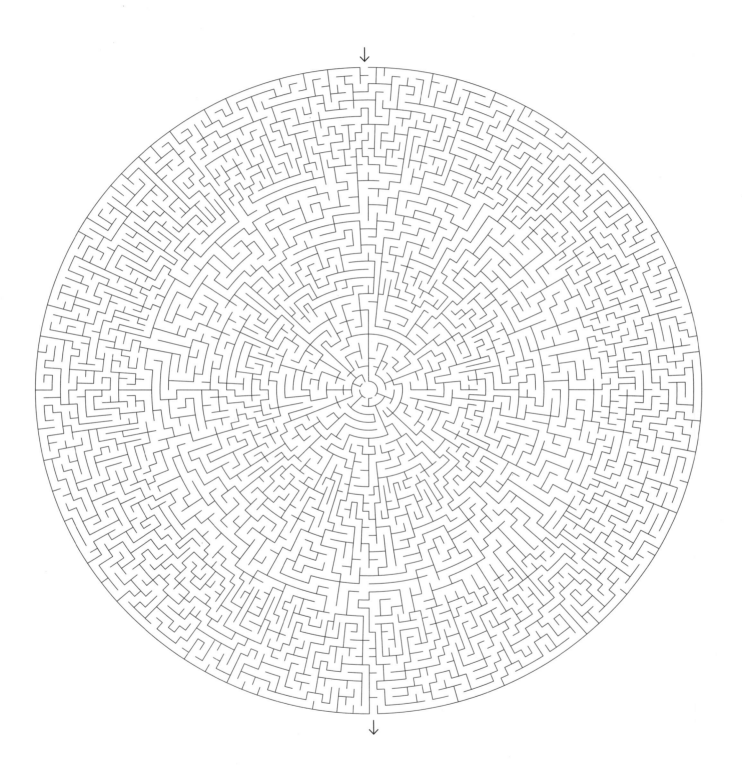

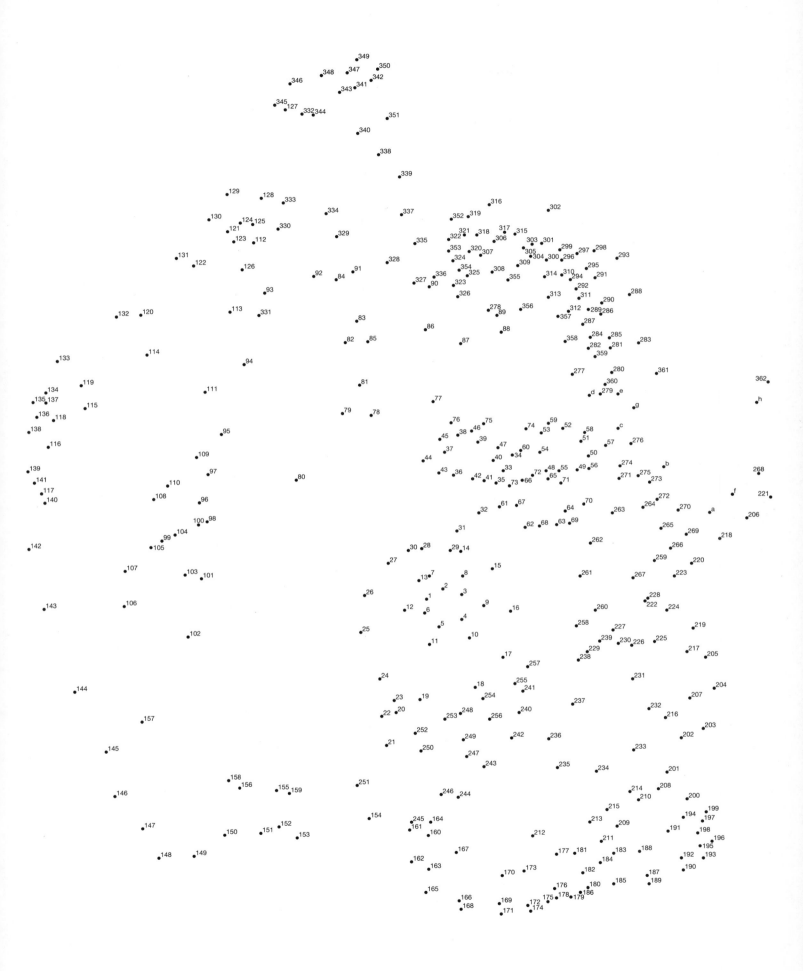

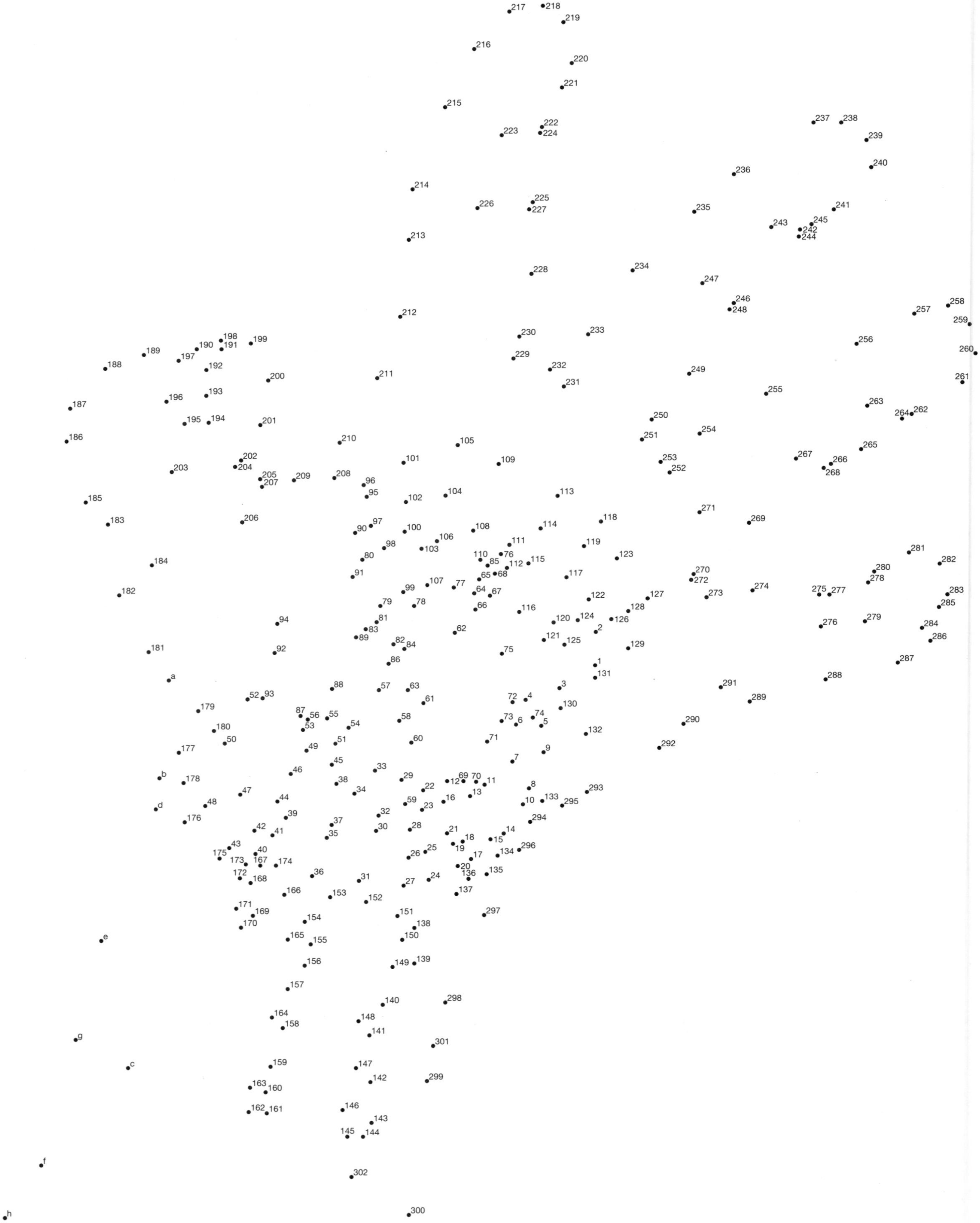

Eldritch Characters

```
H E G P E Y A Z A T H O T H O G T I E E
R R E E N A T U E I N I G D P R H A T H
E A O T O S N G N Y A L U R T T R A I H
L M H O G N D O O U Y E O B O H G H N H
B T S H A N A R O G G G T H R N G M A F
M H T T D H I I A N E A T T I I O G R S
A G S A R N A S H N N O N H E M O R E H
H I I L O Y T S Y T S F T D O G Z E T L
S N M R O T S O T G I R E N Y K O A P R
L Y S A I Y F S O U E D S D E E U T O R
A H S Y H Y R Y E D R T D E M G B R E L
N G E N I E A M L N R P Y A G E L A L H
O U L G O L S E O O K C L O Y T G C O O
I O E H N O L G U O C R H R U E H E C T
S D M O A Y N S E O N T A H B S N O A T
N G A A A H F H T D A B T D H O D F D E
E O N A Z R H O H S N E A E S O Y I O
M R E N O I T L T B S L I A T H Y I H S
I R O G M N I U H L U H T C S A T T T O
D A O G L A Z R H R T O L S Y T E H T Y
```

AZATHOTH

COLEOPTERAN

CTHULHU

DAGON

DIMENSIONAL SHAMBLER

DOUGHY NIGHTMARE

ELDER THING

GLYGAS

GREAT RACE OF YITH

HASTUR

MONSTROUS FROG

MOON-BEAST

NAMELESS MIST

NUG AND YEB

NYARLATHOTEP

PROGENY OF YIG

THE DARKNESS

TSATHOGGUA

YADDITHIAN

YOG-SOTHOTH

ZALGO

ZOOG

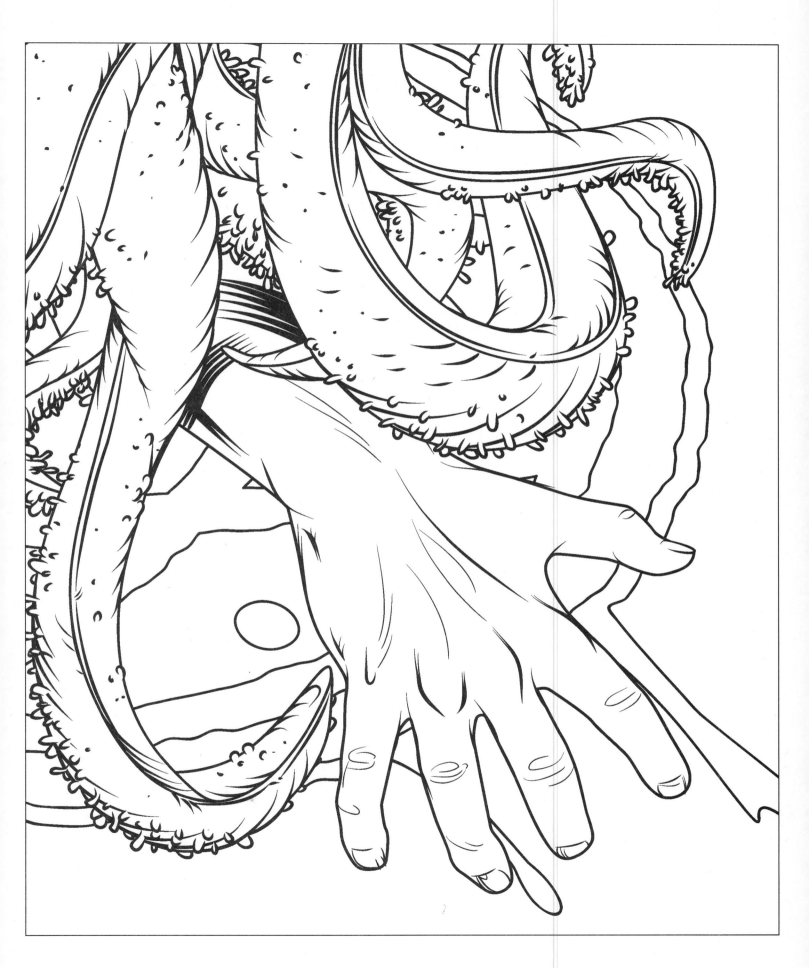

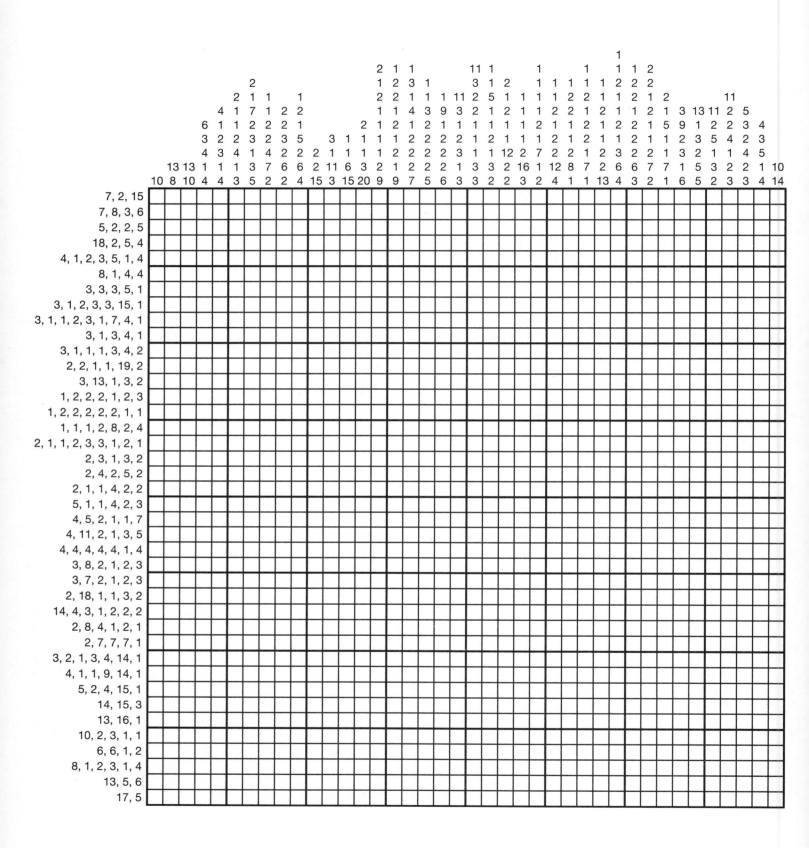

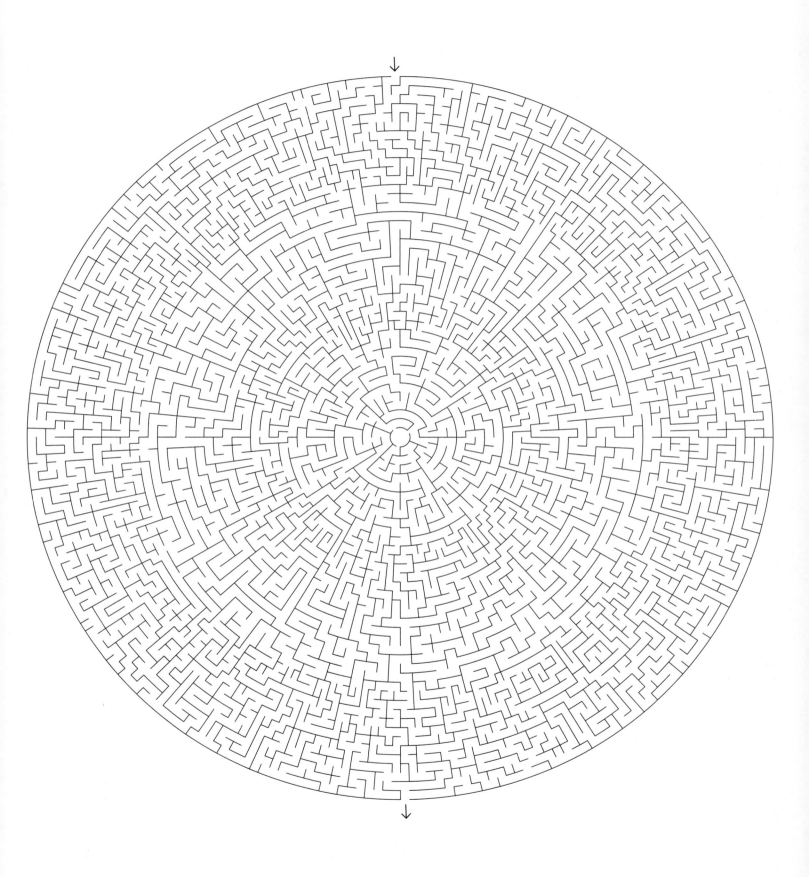

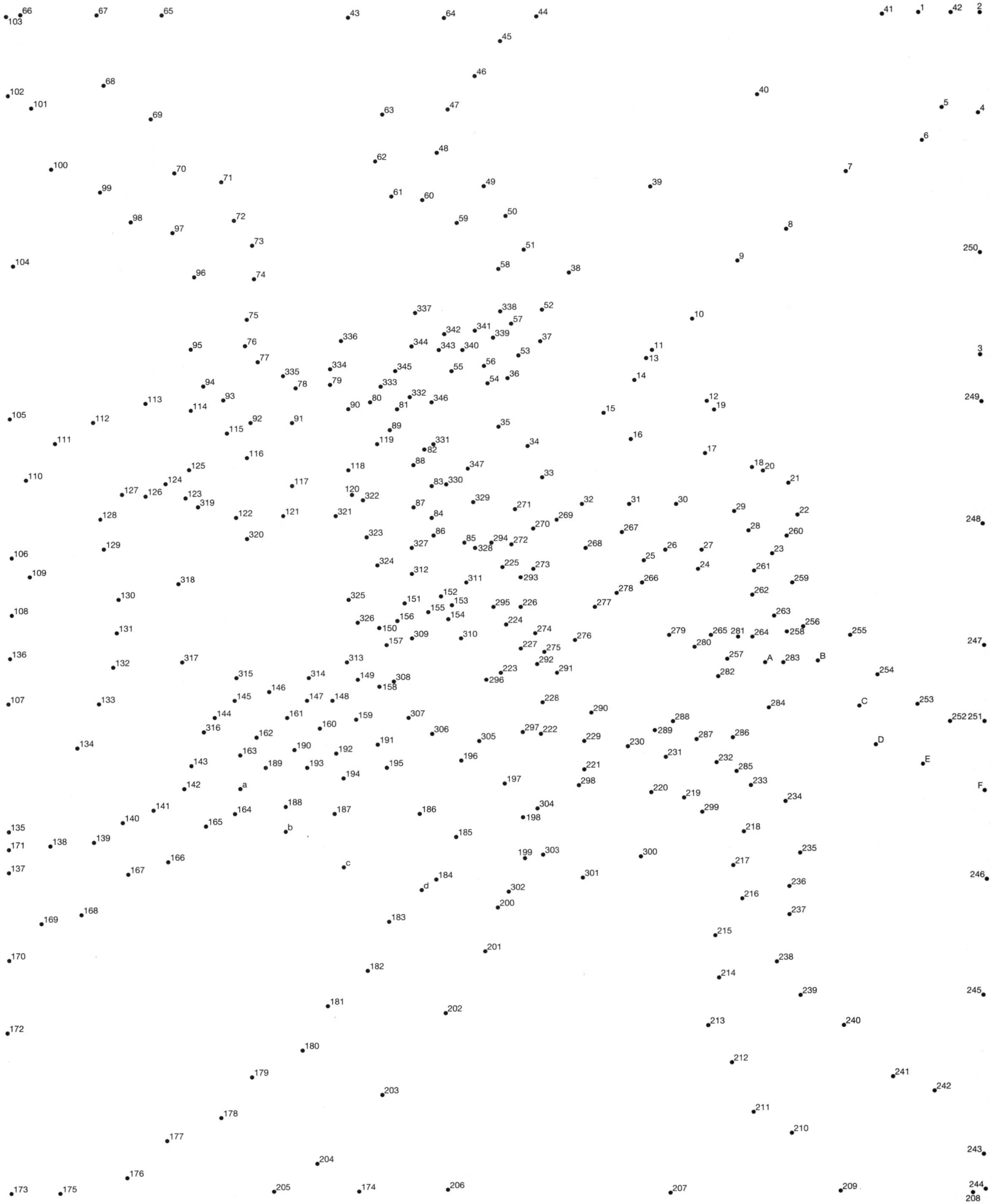

The Call of Cthulhu

```
E U T N A S I S L T M A D H U O U E L E
M A E E H A U R S E H S D T I M U R U D
M T O S D N Y L M P Y E T O C T O P U S
S H W N O D W C L A P N U A T E D A H N
E U E A H G W T W L R E N O T D I W A O
N R I H Y A N R O A T E L P N R E M S E
O S R O H E O L N H P O I A E E U H C C
D T D J A N S G E I A R L T N H L E U N
L O T H E A E A N S C S S U A L I L L D
O N A R A L L C A S I Y E U L O T H P R
T Y L S L E E I U D H U S S O I S T T A
A S E C R Y L N E S T X W S S X I W U G
E S S T L A A T S D M D N T O A A O R O
R T S G R M R A E O H E S N A L R N E N
G U T T L A M C A S S U R N U T I G I I
O E S C H E T H E E M M A S A T W P E E
S U I C A D E I A S A C W I L C O X O L
A G N A N A E D I L C U E N O N L E N L
R U L U R I T U A L E E U H W I M D C H
T H T A H C C S C A S H A I H E Y L R L
```

ANGELL

AUSTRALIA

CULTISTS

DRAGON

GREAT OLD ONE

HUMAN

JOHANSEN

LEGRASSE

MANUSCRIPT

MASS HYSTERIA

NON-EUCLIDEAN

NORWAY

OCTOPUS

RITUAL

R'LYEH

SCULPTURE

THE ALERT

THE EMMA

THURSTON

UNCHARTED ISLAND

WEIRD TALES

WILCOX

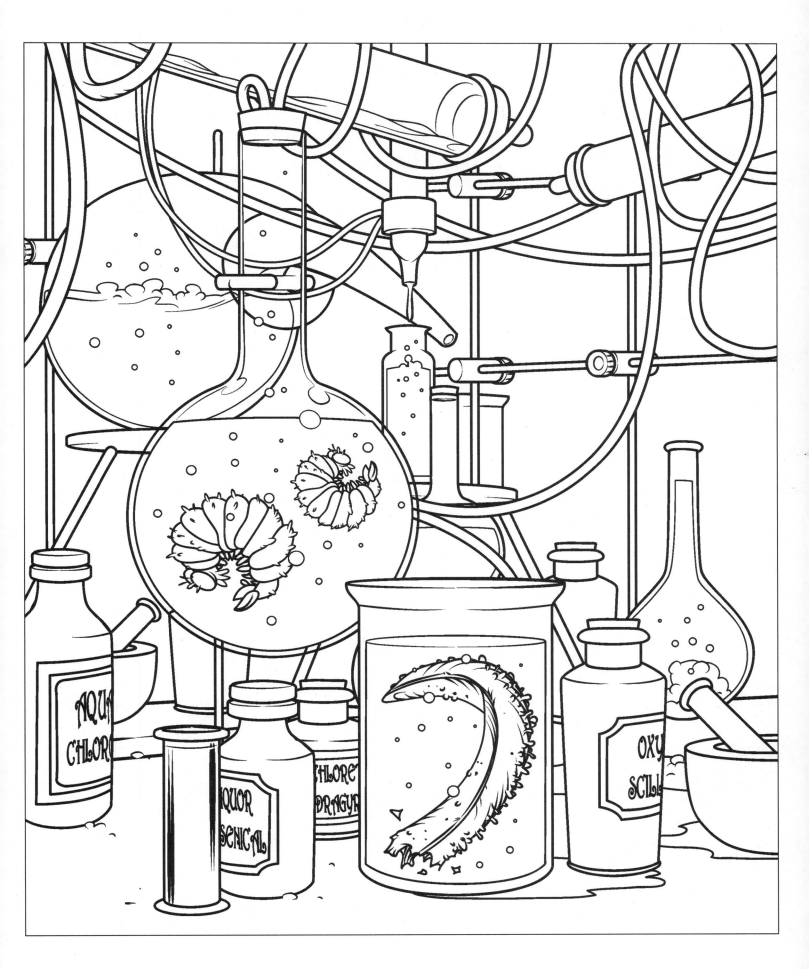

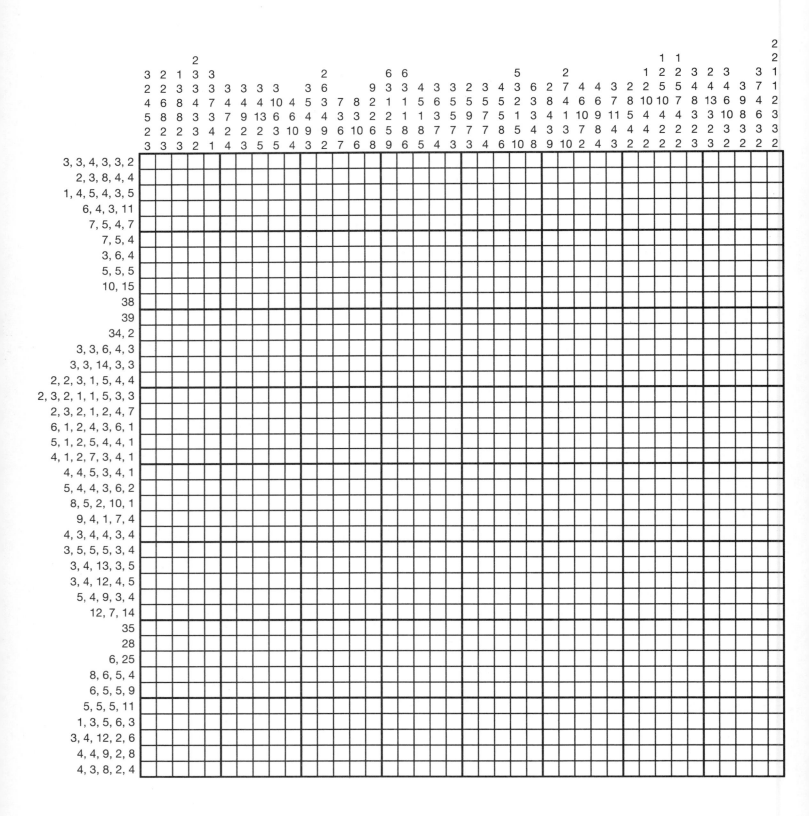

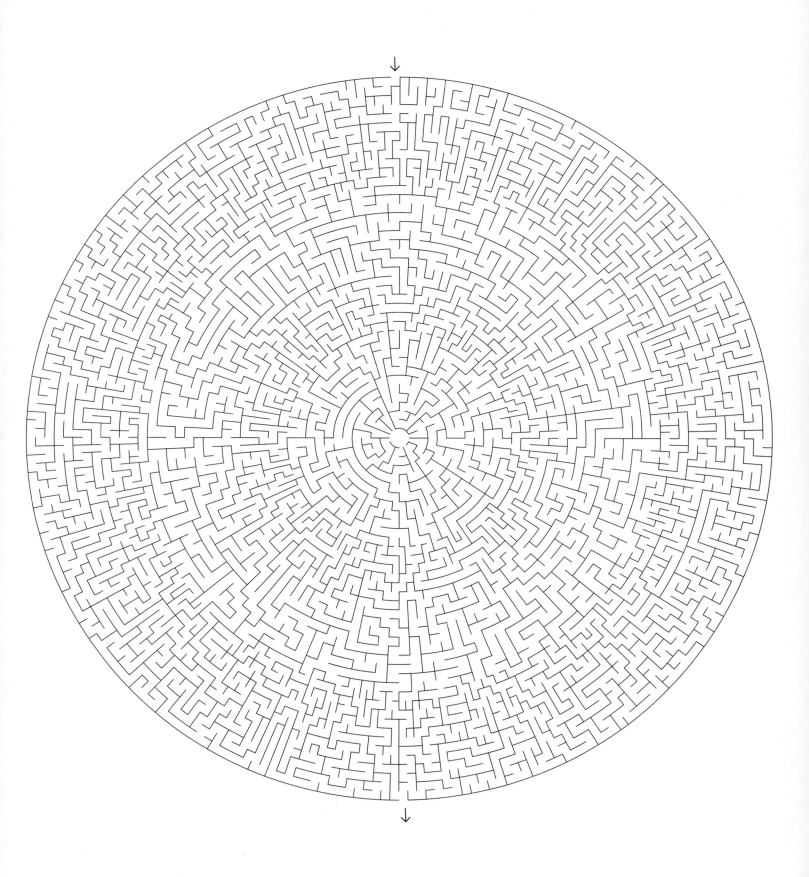

Cthulhu Mythos Characters

```
L R R B F R A N K P A B O D I E H N O G
T E E K A A E H I R E Y D M A I L L I W
T A I H A R L E Y W A R R E N W D W W A
S H D T S R W Y N J E L R S R W C W S L
E A A A I R E L E O B E H L H H I E D T
W S P O N O A I D F S F A A L L N A D E
T F D W G B T M A E A A T L B A N O R R
R U M J E E B A S I A E M U T A S A M G
E D M E D R A F D A L N R H S N N F U I
B A H R E T R N R E B W W H A D R H N L
R E N V S O R Y Y O H A I O O I D J O M
E A E A P L J M A A I R N L Z W Z A Z A
H E B S E M E R T T E U P R L B E E R N
A E A D T S Y E E F T H Y P A S M R K E
R I E U E T L J I L C A L E E B E T D I
N H N D Y E L E T A H W A I N I V A L O
U M T L Y A L H R I O B E D M A R S H T
M T A E U D E T T E L R E D E T M O C R
A D D Y N N E S N A H O J F A T S U G S
B A E D E R Z A H L A L U D B A M J O N
```

ABDUL ALHAZRED	JERVAS DUDLEY
ASENATH WAITE	KEZIAH MASON
BARNABAS MARSH	LAVINIA WHATELEY
COMTE D'ERLETTE	OBED MARSH
DANA SHIREFIELD	OLD WHATELEY
DR MUNOZ	RANDOLPH CARTER
ETEPSED EGNIS	ROBERT OLMSTEAD
FRANK PABODIE	THE JERMYN FAMILY
GUSTAF JOHANSEN	WALTER GILMAN
HARLEY WARREN	WILBUR WHATELEY
HERBERT WEST	WILLIAM DYER

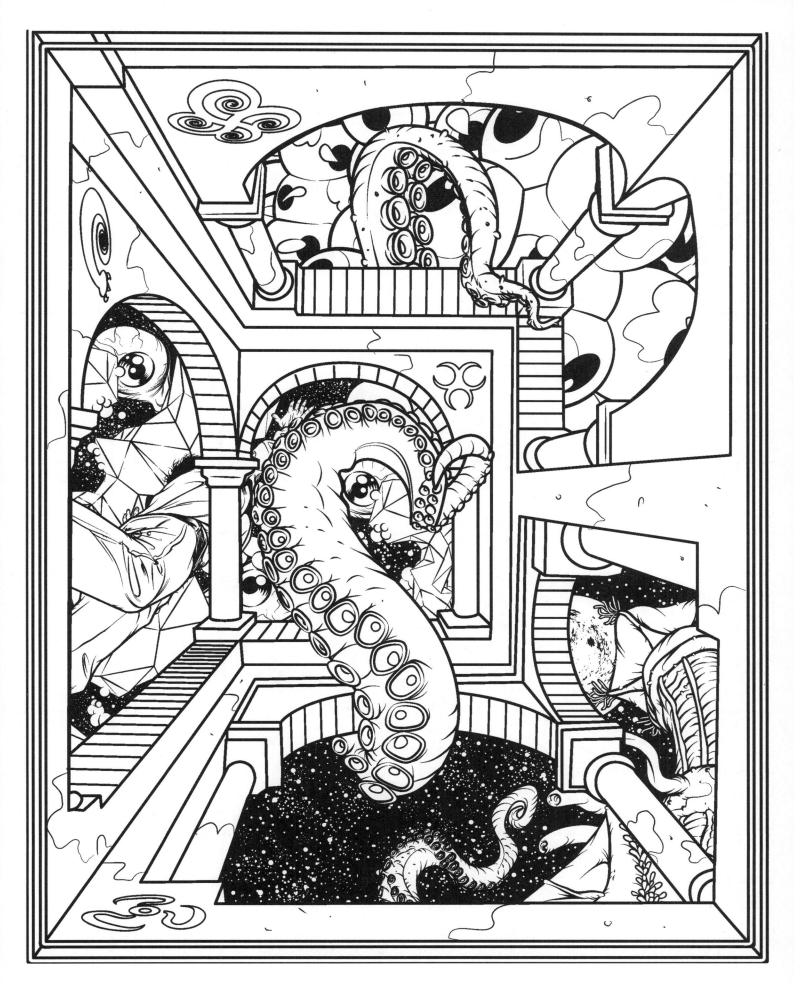

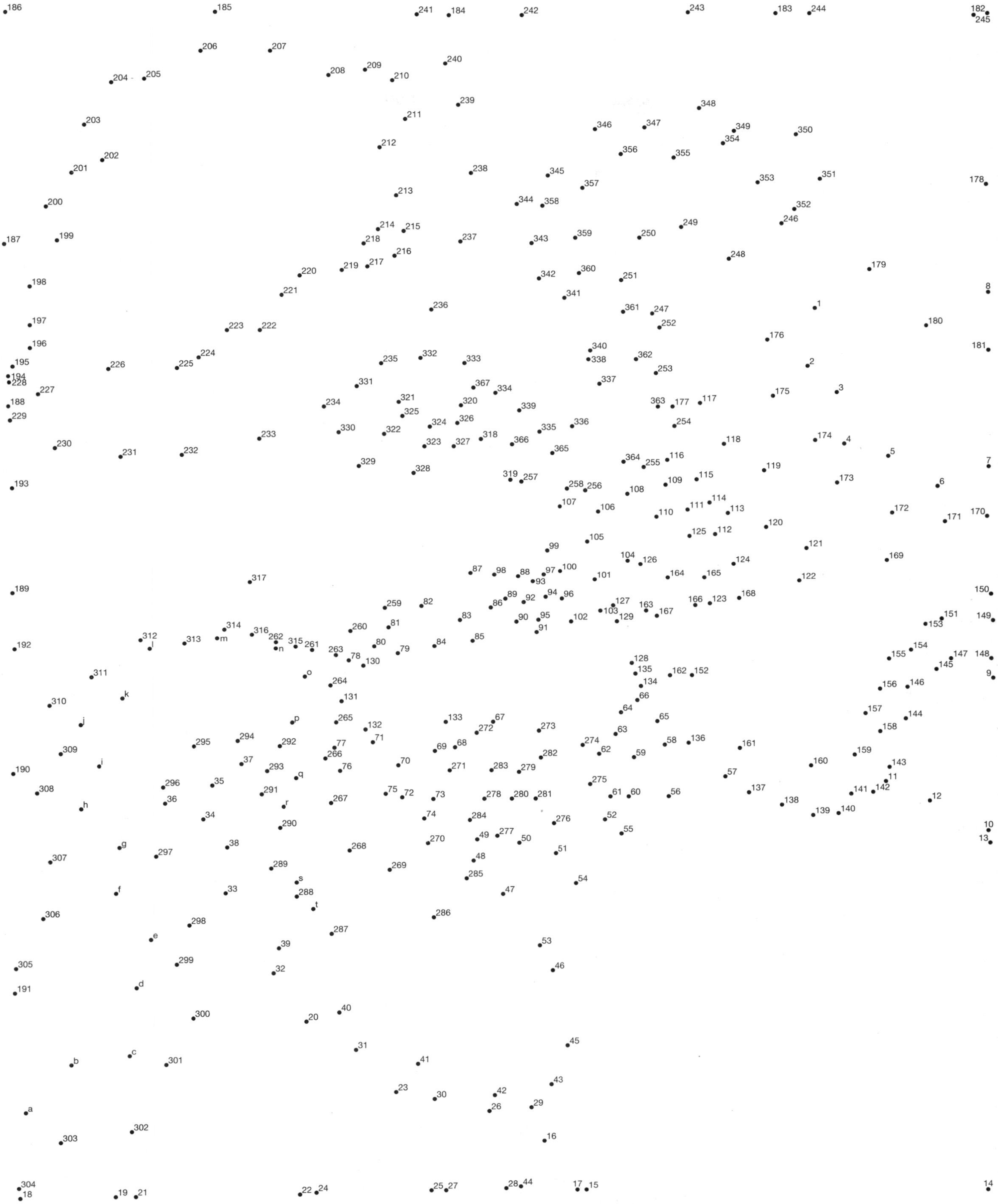

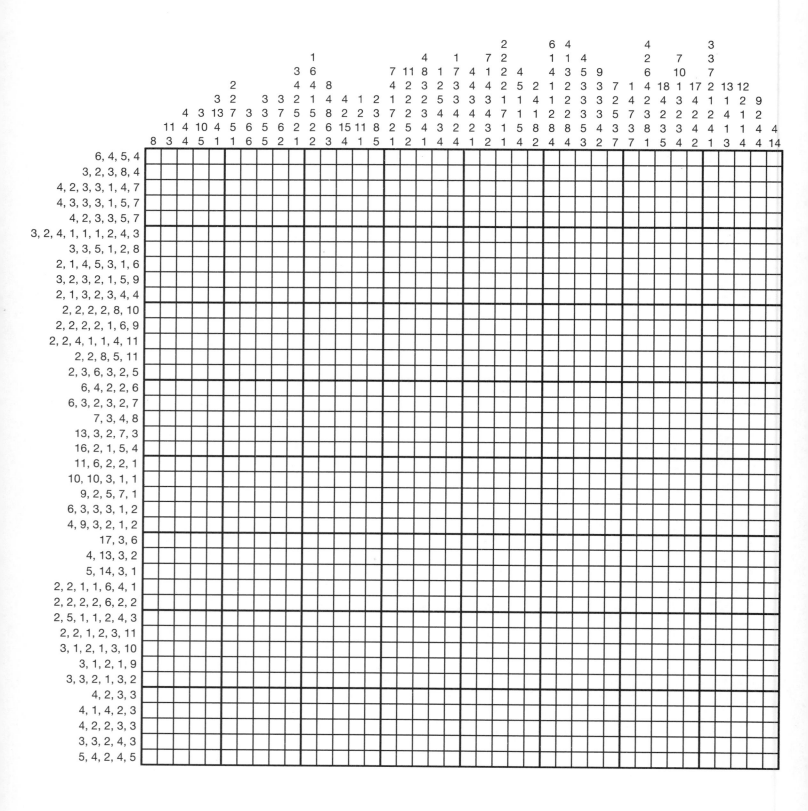

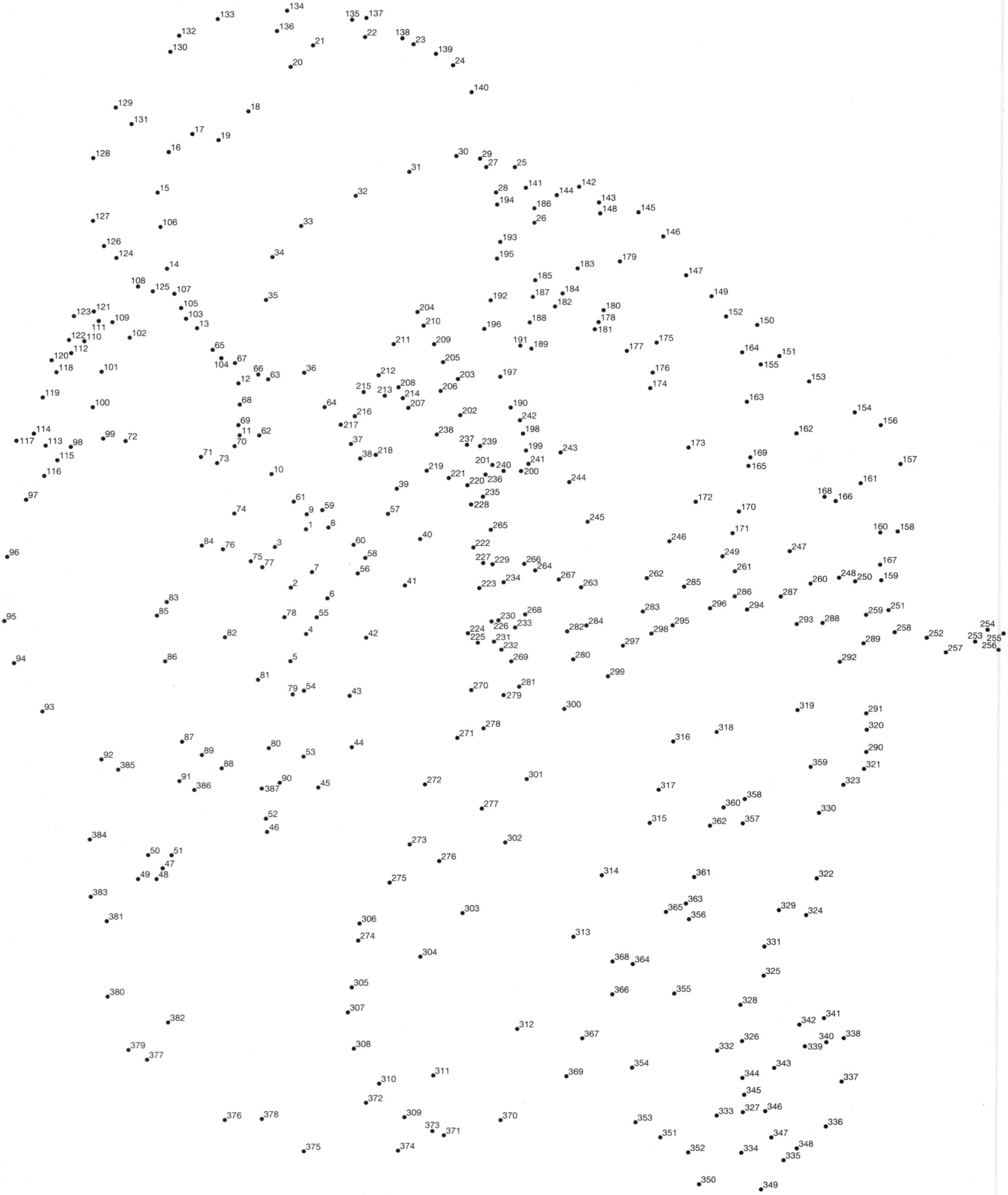

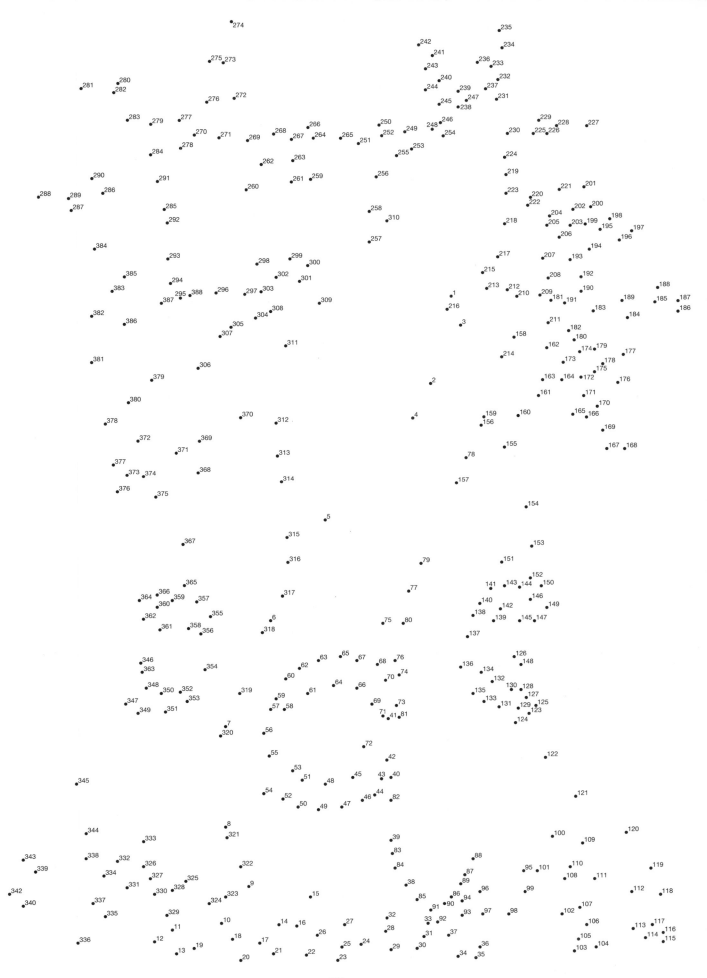

Forms of Nyarlathotep in Literature

```
R H E R I H E T E S S L A L O E L D N W
E D F T B T O E N O S S E L N I K S M K
H S O N A L S W H D G N P E L L A O C A
M U S G D H O I L E R I C H R T B R I M
M O O H S N F A M E A E B K O A L N D R
A A A S R S A O T G R T L L G L A O N O
H H B I E R E M Y E N I E I G R C H I F
L K R T L E N L E G D I N E C A K K W E
I H I K W H I O E T I W L T A N M T K T
T O N L A T D H M C I F O W H T A N C D
N A G E R I A N T E A H F M A E N S A E
N R E A C R R R E S D F W E A R D O L D
E A R M L W K E N T A K E E A N C A B T
N H O A L G D H N A I E C H H T P D R P
O P F S A N E G E C R K B A T T W U K K
K K P S M I M K R W A O E E L O G T O E
R C E I S L O R L T E A G W H B M W B O
A A S R A I N T N A A O T U K T E D S R
D L T M E A W A A E I N E S H B M H W L
W B S F T W W S A H T U D G B S S T T A
```

AHTU	L'ROG'G
BLACK MAN	NARLA
BLACK PHARAOH	SAMAEL
BLACK WIND	SHUGORAN
BLOATED WOMAN	SKINLESS ONE
BRINGER OF PESTS	SMALL CRAWLER
CRAWLING MIST	THE BEAST
DARK DEMON	THE BLACK DEMON
DARK ONE	THE FACELESS GOD
EFFIGY OF HATE	THE WHITE MAN
HOWLER IN THE DARK	WAILING WRITHER

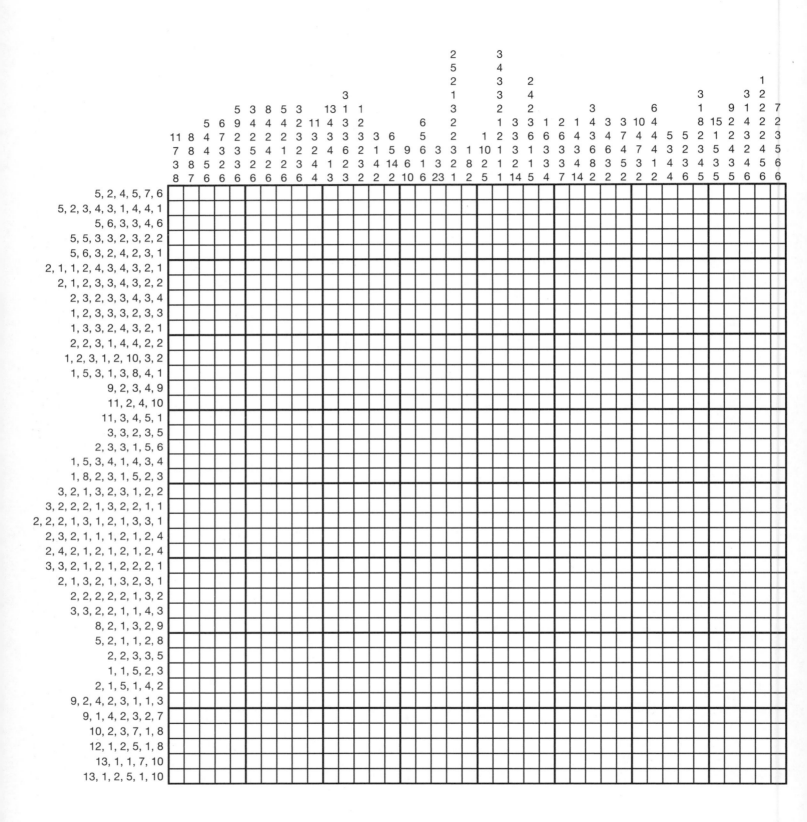

Cthulhu Outer Gods

```
M A A H T Z A Z H O R R A T H A S T K P
G B H H U S R P H R S G T N H R H N T H
O G R I R S H S E Y N A E N H H H N N T
R N H I A S D H R T G T R Y T T Y T R H
R I T Y H I I T T H O Y A O H T O U N N
L H I H T N Y Y H A A H H A I E N K A R
N T H T A N L G A O A B T L N E B A L N
A D M O O G T T Z A A N A A M K Y A N O
H U R H G A O Y H R N H C B L H Y R S D
K O H T L N A A N L A P R U O R I O R A
U L T A U C B N K A R A L U S S A U H H
D C R Z K Y H T K T N D N I A T T Y R G
L E O A T L T H K Y L D K X H S R B N I
A H G G H Y T R I M E R A C Y T E I H L
A T A T U I A E Y H U B B O S A T H L A
H D D B B O N G Y R K O R A T H A E B X
N L L B T R L H S R G L T H E H Y D R A
O D A A A A L K T Y O M A G N T H O H H
Y H I D A R K N E S S O A E H H H Y D I
S T H S O I L E T C Y N O G O A I A G M
```

ABHOTH

AZATHOTH

AZHORRA-THA

DARKNESS

IALDAGORTH

LU-KTHU

MH'ITHRHA

NGYR-KORATH

NYARLATHOTEP

NYCTELIOS

OLKOTH

SHABBITH-KA

SUC'NAATH

THE CLOUD-THING

THE HYDRA

TRU'NEMBRA

UBBO-SATHLA

XA'LIGHA

YCNAGNNISSSZ

YHOUNDEH

YIDHRA

YOMAGN'THO

THE DAEMON

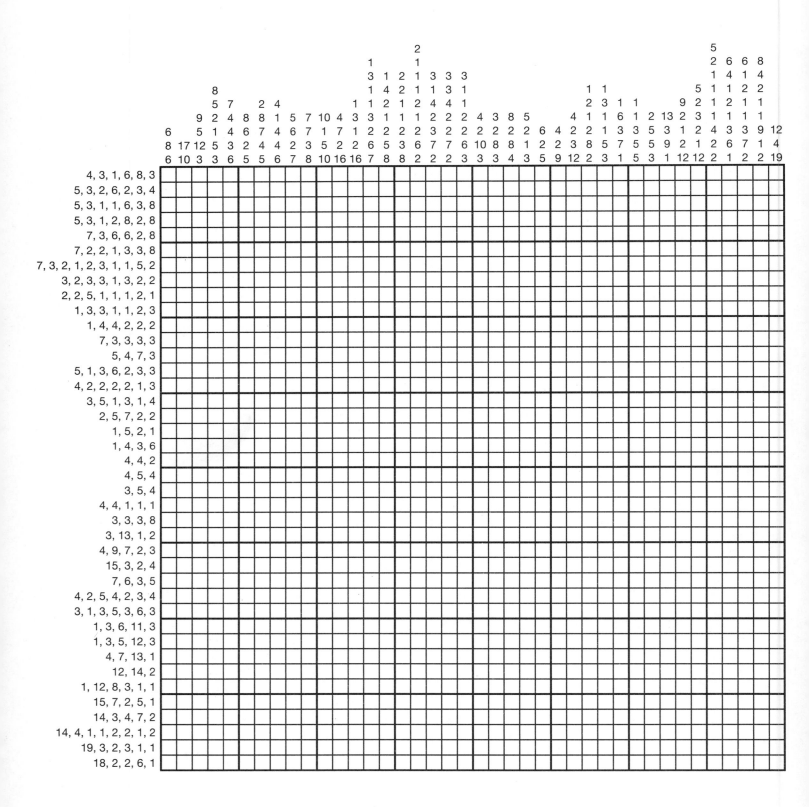

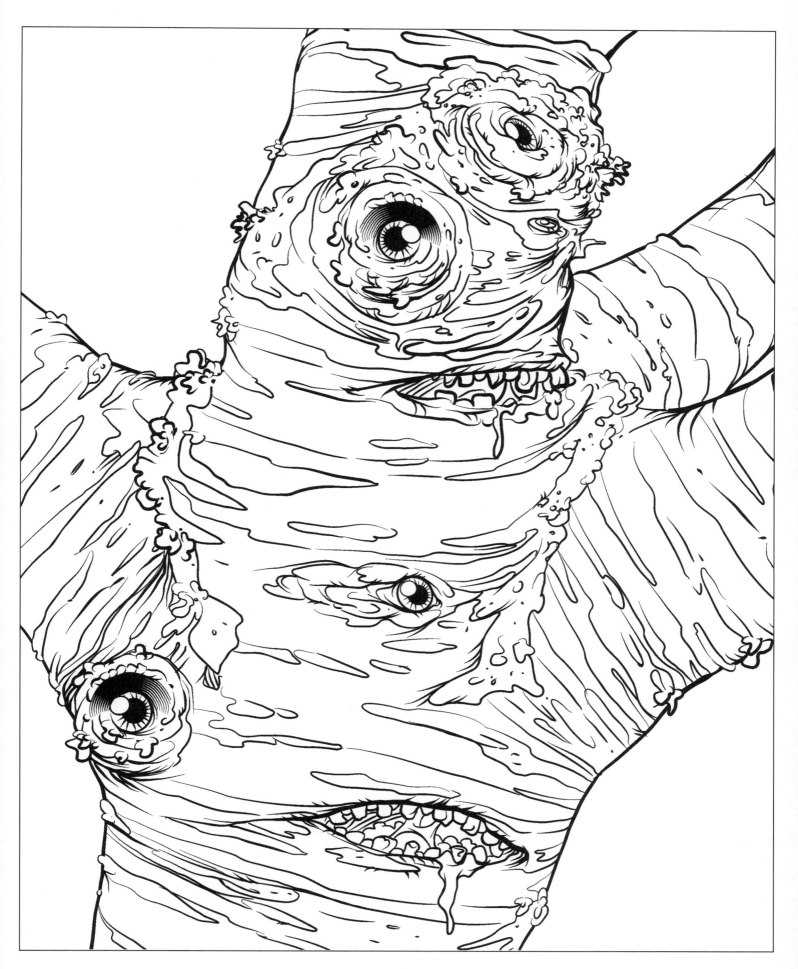

SOLUTIONS

7

8

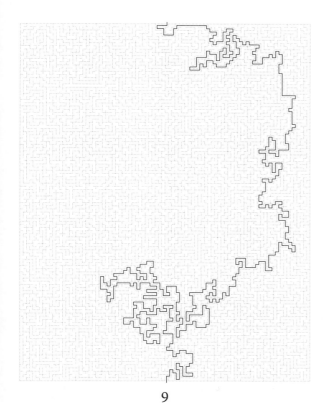

9

11

12

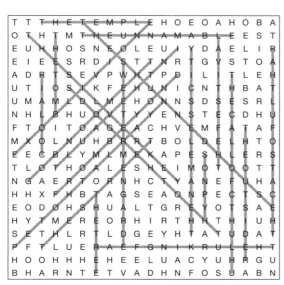

13

14

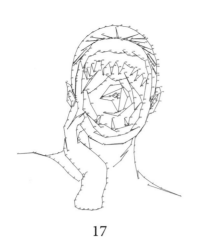

17

18

20

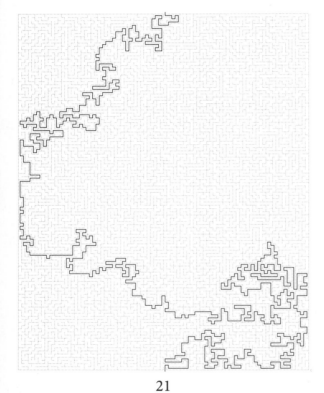

21

23

24

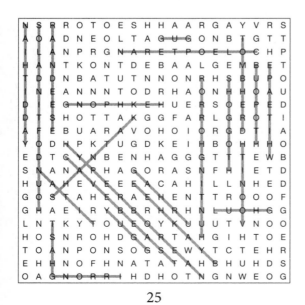

25

26

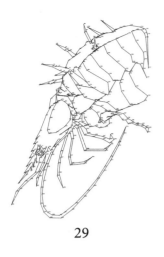

29

30

32

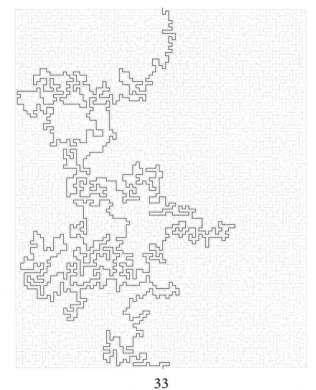

33

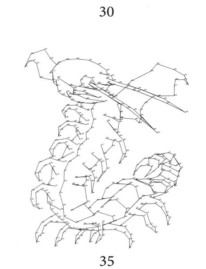

35

36

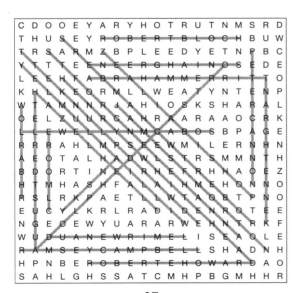

37

38

41

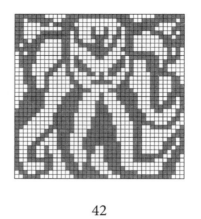

42

44

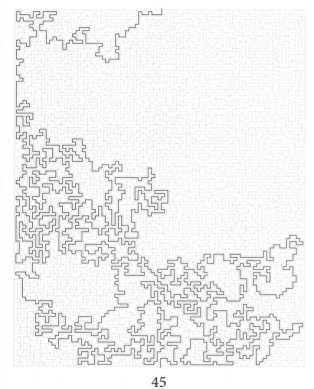

45

47

48

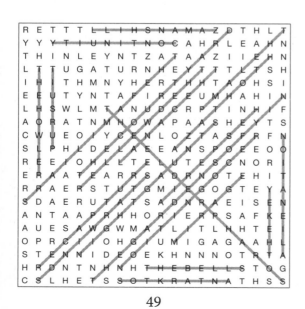

49

50

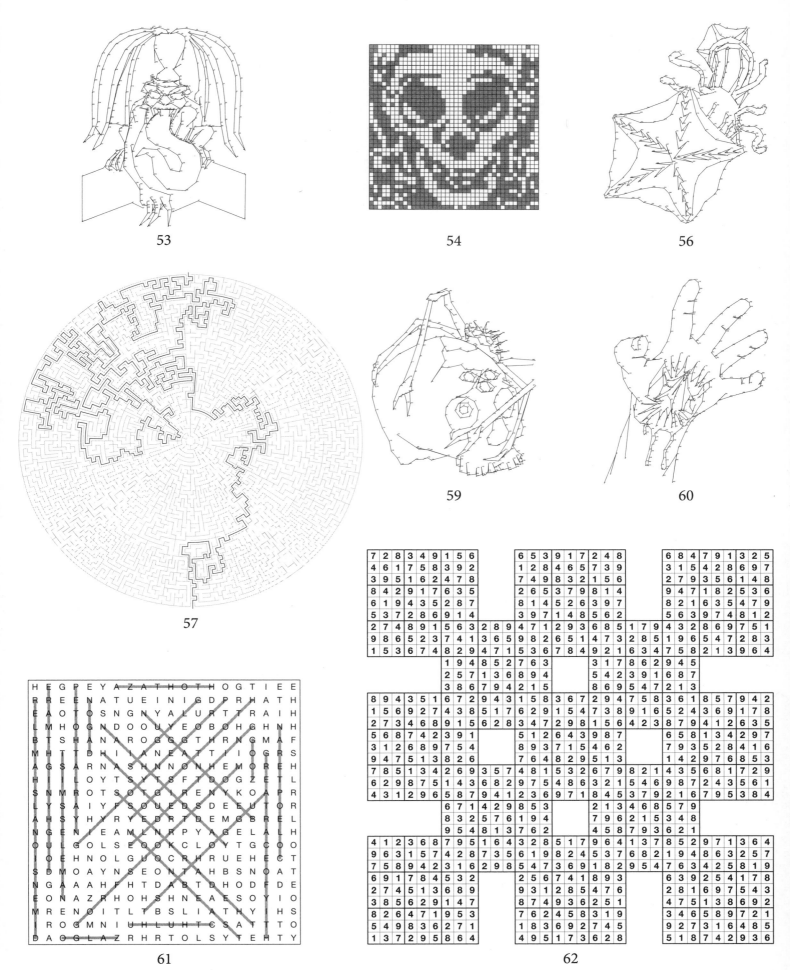

53

54

56

57

59

60

61

62

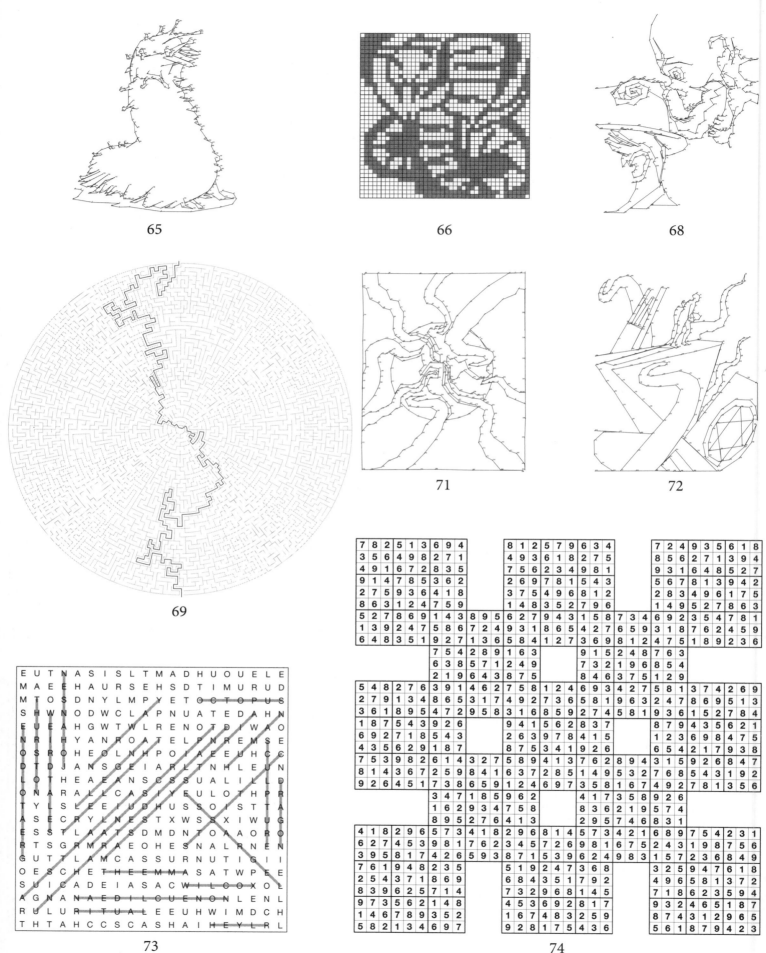

65

66

68

69

71

72

73

74

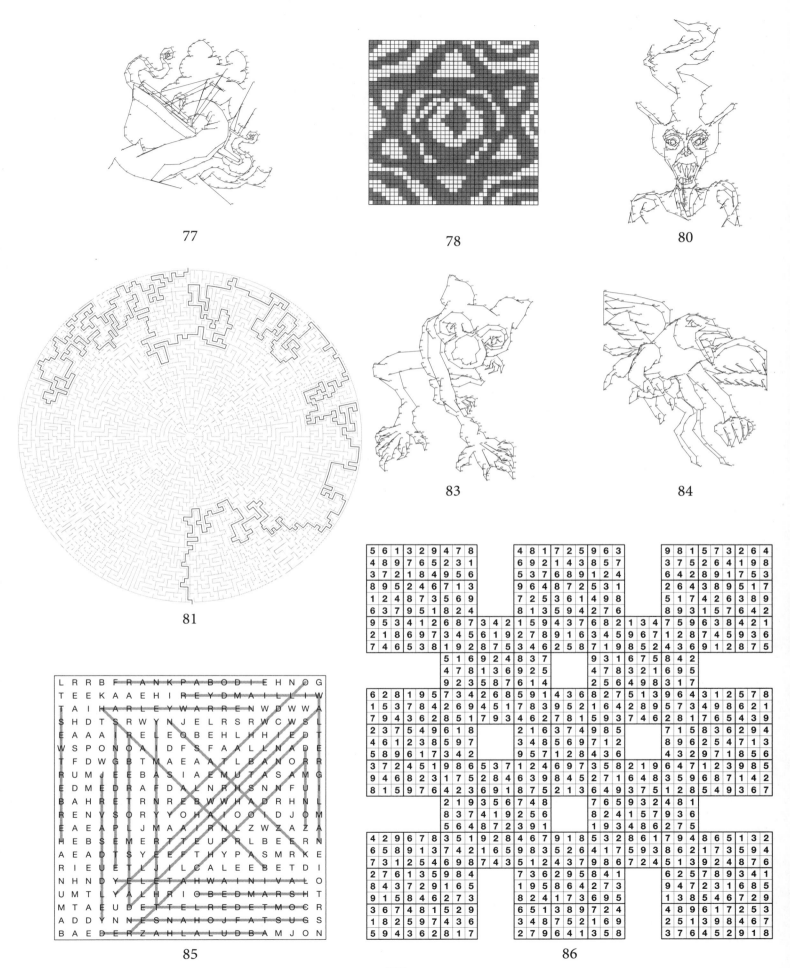

77

78

80

81

83

84

85

86

89

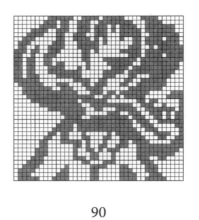

90

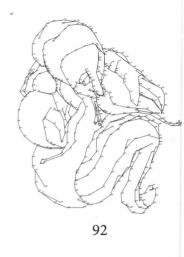

92

93

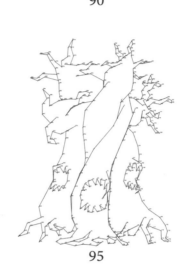

95

96

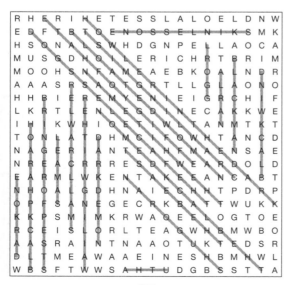

97

98

101

102

104

105

107

108

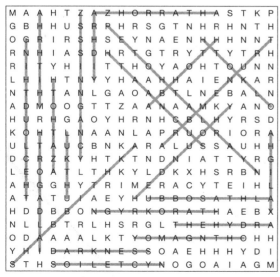

M	A	A	H	T	Z	A	Z	H	O	R	R	A	T	H	A	S	T	K	P
G	B	H	H	U	S	R	R	H	R	S	G	T	N	H	R	H	N	T	H
O	G	R	I	R	S	H	S	E	Y	N	A	E	N	H	H	H	N	N	T
R	N	H	I	A	S	D	H	R	T	G	T	R	Y	T	T	Y	T	R	H
R	I	T	Y	H	I	I	T	T	H	O	Y	A	O	H	T	O	U	N	N
L	H	I	H	T	N	Y	Y	H	A	A	H	H	A	I	E	N	K	A	R
N	T	H	T	A	N	L	G	A	O	A	B	T	L	N	E	B	A	L	N
A	D	M	O	O	G	T	T	Z	A	A	N	A	A	M	K	Y	A	N	O
H	U	R	H	G	A	O	Y	H	R	N	H	C	B	L	H	Y	R	S	D
K	O	H	T	L	N	A	A	N	L	A	P	R	U	O	R	I	O	R	A
U	L	T	A	U	C	B	N	K	A	R	A	L	U	S	S	A	U	H	H
D	C	R	Z	K	Y	H	T	K	T	N	D	N	I	A	T	T	Y	R	G
L	E	O	A	T	L	T	H	K	Y	L	D	K	X	H	S	R	B	N	I
A	H	G	G	H	Y	T	R	I	M	E	R	A	C	Y	T	E	I	H	L
A	T	A	T	U	I	A	E	Y	H	U	B	B	O	S	A	T	H	L	A
H	D	D	B	B	O	N	G	Y	R	K	O	R	A	T	H	A	E	B	X
N	L	L	B	T	R	L	H	S	R	G	L	T	H	E	H	Y	D	R	A
O	D	A	A	A	A	L	K	T	Y	O	M	A	G	N	T	H	O	H	H
Y	H	I	D	A	R	K	N	E	S	S	O	A	E	H	H	H	Y	D	I
S	T	H	S	O	I	L	E	T	C	Y	N	O	G	O	A	I	A	G	M

109

3	8	6	5	9	7	2	4	1				8	5	6	3	9	4	2	1	7				5	9	3	4	6	8	1	7	2
7	4	9	1	6	2	8	5	3				2	4	1	6	5	7	8	9	3				1	8	6	7	3	2	9	4	5
2	5	1	8	3	4	6	7	9				9	3	7	1	2	8	5	6	4				7	2	4	5	9	1	8	3	6
9	3	8	4	7	1	5	2	6				5	7	9	8	1	6	4	3	2				6	1	9	3	2	7	4	5	8
5	1	4	6	2	8	3	9	7				3	1	8	5	4	2	6	7	9				2	4	7	6	8	5	3	9	1
6	7	2	9	5	3	1	8	4				4	6	2	9	7	3	1	8	5				8	3	5	9	1	4	2	6	7
8	6	5	7	1	9	4	3	2	1	9	6	7	8	5	4	6	9	3	2	1	5	6	4	9	7	8	1	4	6	5	2	3
4	9	3	2	8	6	7	1	5	3	8	2	6	9	4	2	3	1	7	5	8	3	9	2	4	6	1	2	5	3	7	8	9
1	2	7	3	4	5	9	6	8	5	4	7	1	2	3	7	8	5	9	4	6	8	1	7	3	5	2	8	7	9	6	1	4
						5	2	4	8	6	3	9	1	7				8	6	5	1	7	3	2	4	9						
						6	7	3	9	2	1	4	5	8				4	7	9	2	8	6	5	1	3						
						1	8	9	7	5	4	2	3	6				1	3	2	9	4	5	6	8	7						
5	1	4	8	3	7	2	9	6	4	3	8	5	7	1	2	4	9	6	8	3	4	2	1	7	9	5	4	3	2	6	1	8
7	2	3	9	5	6	8	4	1	2	7	5	3	6	9	7	5	8	2	1	4	7	5	9	8	3	6	1	5	7	4	9	2
6	9	8	4	1	2	3	5	7	6	1	9	8	4	2	6	1	3	5	9	7	6	3	8	1	2	4	8	6	9	3	5	7
8	5	7	3	9	1	6	2	4				6	9	5	4	3	1	7	2	8				3	6	8	2	4	5	9	7	1
2	6	9	5	7	4	1	3	8				7	1	3	8	9	2	4	5	6				9	5	7	6	8	1	2	3	4
3	4	1	6	2	8	5	7	9				4	2	8	5	6	7	1	3	9				2	4	1	9	7	3	5	8	6
9	7	5	1	6	3	4	8	2	1	5	6	9	3	7	1	2	4	8	6	5	7	9	3	4	1	2	5	9	8	7	6	3
1	8	2	7	4	5	9	6	3	7	8	2	1	5	4	3	8	6	9	7	2	6	1	4	5	8	3	7	2	6	1	4	9
4	3	6	2	8	9	7	1	5	9	3	4	2	8	6	9	7	5	3	4	1	8	2	5	6	7	9	3	1	4	8	2	5
						1	9	4	5	2	8	6	7	3				6	2	8	3	4	7	1	9	5						
						2	3	8	6	7	1	5	4	9				7	9	3	1	5	6	2	4	8						
						6	5	7	3	4	9	8	2	1				1	5	4	9	8	2	7	3	6						
2	6	9	4	5	3	8	7	1	4	6	5	3	9	2	6	4	8	5	1	7	2	3	9	8	6	4	9	7	3	2	5	1
5	4	7	1	6	8	3	2	9	8	1	7	4	6	5	7	1	3	2	8	9	4	6	1	3	5	7	1	2	4	6	8	9
3	8	1	9	2	7	5	4	6	2	9	3	7	1	8	9	2	5	4	3	6	5	7	8	9	2	1	5	8	6	7	3	4
4	5	2	7	1	9	6	8	3				8	7	9	2	6	4	3	5	1				4	8	2	7	5	9	3	1	6
9	7	8	6	3	2	4	1	5				6	2	1	5	3	9	7	4	8				1	3	9	6	4	8	5	2	7
1	3	6	8	4	5	2	9	7				5	4	3	8	7	1	9	6	2				5	7	6	2	3	1	9	4	8
6	1	3	2	7	4	9	5	8				9	5	4	1	8	2	6	7	3				7	1	3	8	9	5	4	6	2
8	2	5	3	9	1	7	6	4				2	8	6	3	5	7	1	9	4				6	9	5	4	1	2	8	7	3
7	9	4	5	8	6	1	3	2				1	3	7	4	9	6	8	2	5				2	4	8	3	6	7	1	9	5

110

113

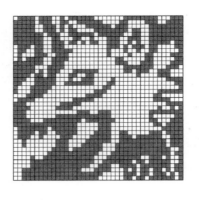

114

116

117